A Story, a Hug and a Prayer

A Family Bedtime Book

Michael Forster

Illustrated by
Jennifer Carter

First published in 1994 by
KEVIN MAYHEW LTD
Rattlesden
Bury St Edmunds
Suffolk IP30 0SZ

ISBN   0 86209 505 0

Editor Jo Donlevy
Typesetting and Page Creation by Anne Haskell
Printed and bound in Great Britain.

FOREWORD

P|raying with the children is a lot more – and can be a lot more enjoyable – than simply reciting sets of words. It's something to be done *together*. God wants to be involved in all our relationships. So don't just talk to God – talk to each other, laugh, play, *enjoy* one another – and God will join in! The prayers themselves are very short. Much more important are the interactions which can surround them. Don't be afraid to explore events, feelings, ideas. Feel free to break off, if reading the prayer aloud, and ask a question, or make a comment. Feel equally free to use gestures, hugs, and so on, as well as words. For example, in the David and Goliath session, some children will probably choose fights over cuddles – don't be afraid to indulge in some playful sparring, or even a pillow-fight. You can then make the point that in some kinds of fights, people get hurt.

Since the obvious time for these prayers is bedtime, try to keep the *We're Sad* part positive. The idea is to say 'Sorry', and then sleep well, not to stir up guilt! So emphasise forgiveness rather than guilt, and how about finishing this section with a cuddle?

The Bedtime Stories are deliberately expanded somewhat, to make them more enjoyable for children. They are imaginative re-tellings of the originals, including many details which have not come from the bible but which add colour – and hopefully will stimulate children's imaginations. However, the essential point of each story has been carefully preserved and in many cases actually highlighted. In this most important respect, the stories are all faithful to their scriptural base.

Praying with children is a wonderful opportunity not only to build up their faith, but to deepen relationships within the family. Use this book as freely as you like. The worst thing you can do is simply recite it!

MICHAEL FORSTER

CONTENTS

OLD TESTAMENT

NEW TESTAMENT

Jesus is Born

Things Jesus Did

Stories Jesus Told

After the Ascension

A BOATFUL OF TROUBLE

A| very long time ago, there was a man called Noah. He lived with his wife, whom everyone called Mrs. Noah (because they were terribly polite in those days) and his three sons. His sons were called Shem, Ham and Japheth. Each of them was married, and can you guess what their wives were called?

Noah was a good man; he and his family tried to live the way God wanted. They loved each other, looked after the land, cared for their animals and tried to make life as good for everyone as they could.

One day, God spoke to Noah. 'The trouble is,' he said, 'that not everyone's as caring as you are. People cheat and steal; they're cruel to each other and to the animals; they want the earth to give them lots of food, but they don't want to look after it. If they go on this way, there'll be no earth left. I want you to build a boat.'

Now, if Noah hadn't known better, he'd have thought God was talking nonsense. 'A boat?' he said, 'Here? Now what would I do with a boat, when there's nowhere to sail it?'

'Give me time,' said God, 'and there will be! There's going to be a flood – and you'll need the boat to live in.'

'Why a boat?' asked Noah? 'We can go and live on the mountain.'

'It's going to be a big flood,' said God, 'and the water is going to be everywhere. If I were you, I'd stop wasting time arguing and get on with building the boat. You'd better make it good and big, because you're taking a lot of animals with you.'

'How many?' asked Noah.

'Two,' God answered. But before Noah could say that they wouldn't need a big boat for just two animals, God went on, '. . . of every kind of creature on earth.'

Now that *did* sound like a lot, but it was obviously no good arguing, so Noah got on with building the boat.

All the family helped, cutting the wood, building the animal pens, making it all watertight. No-one had much time to rest, because it was such a big boat and there wasn't much time to build it.

Of course, the neighbours loved it. They really thought Noah had gone mad! 'Oh!' they shouted, 'Look at Admiral Noah!' They stopped laughing though, and started getting really worried, when the animals started to arrive. After all, zoos are very nice in their place, but who wants to live next door to one? They were quite glad when Noah and his family started loading them into the boat.

How many animals can you think of?

Well, they were all there – two of each. What a job it must have been keeping the foxes away from the chickens and stopping the mice from annoying the elephants! But eventually, they were all on board and Noah closed the hatches, just as it started to rain.

Rain? You've never seen rain like it – day after day for well over a month. Before long, there was no land to be seen and the boat was floating gently on top of the water. But it was no pleasure-cruise – Noah and his family had lots of work to do! Can you imagine looking after all those animals? And they had to make sure they were fed on time, especially the lions, or dreadful things might have happened!

The idea might have seemed like a lot of fun, but everybody soon got pretty fed up with it. No matter how hard Noah tried, the animals just wouldn't learn to get along together. The monkeys kept stealing Noah's bananas (and Noah liked bananas very much); the hyenas kept everyone awake at night, telling jokes and laughing loudly; the giraffes, of course, could see more than anyone else and they gossiped about all the other animals; the elephants wouldn't stay in the middle of the boat and kept making it lop-sided; and Noah threatened to swat the flies, when they annoyed him. Don't you think he should have done?

Everyone was very glad when the water went down and they could all get off the ark. The animals all went their separate ways and Noah said, 'Well, what do we do now?'

'What do you think?' God answered. 'You've got the chance to start again. You can make the world a much better place than it was before.'

Noah thought, 'That's all very well, but how do we know God won't send another flood, if we get it wrong?' But he didn't say that, because he thought it might not be very polite. God knew what he was thinking and said, 'I'm never going to do this again. And to show you I mean it, I'm giving you a rainbow.'

A beautiful rainbow appeared in the sky. And now, all this time later, when the rainbow appears in the sky, it reminds us that God loves us and wants us to be happy.

Based on Genesis 6:9-8:22

Let's Chat

Do you like animals? Do you have any favourites?
Can you imagine a world without any of them?

We're Glad

Loving God,
you made the world,
full of colours –
plants,
animals,
and us.
We're glad about that.
Thank you for our wonderful world.

We're Sad

Sometimes we don't care for the world.
Sometimes we make it dirty,
sometimes we're cruel,
sometimes we just don't notice.
We're sorry.
Help us to care for it better.

Let's Pray for People

Thank you, God,
for people who care:
those who care for animals,
those who grow flowers and food,
those who teach us,
and help us to understand.
Help them to do a good job,
let them know we're grateful.
And help us to care more. Amen.

AIN'T LOVE GRAND?

*T*his is a story about somebody who really loved someone else, and who really showed it as well. His name was Jacob. He was rather a sly character and if he could cheat someone he would. He'd even cheated his own brother, and his father! Then he met Rachel and her older sister, Leah. Leah was a lovely person, with dark and gentle eyes, but it was Rachel that Jacob really noticed. In fact, he did more than notice. He fell head-over-heels in love – which was not surprising, because she was amazingly beautiful, rather like a princess in a pantomime, except that she was real! She had long, dark hair, beautiful smooth skin and, when she smiled, Jacob thought the whole world had lit up! Jacob wanted to marry Rachel, more than he had ever wanted anything else in the whole world.

Rachel's father was called Laban and, although Jacob did not know it, Laban could be a cunning sort of guy, as well. Jacob went to Laban and said, 'I think Rachel is the most beautiful woman I've ever seen, and I want to marry her.' 'Well,' said Laban, 'you'll have to work for her. I'll tell you what: if you work for me for seven years, you can marry Rachel at the end of it.'

Well! What do you think of that? Not a lot, perhaps, but in those days, girls could not do anything unless their fathers agreed – certainly not get married! So Jacob agreed to work seven years for Laban, because he loved Rachel so much.

The seven years went very quickly, because Jacob was so in love with Rachel that he worked really hard. He looked after the sheep, went to the well for water, mended broken fences – whatever needed to be done, he did. Then, when the seven years were up, the wedding was arranged. That's when Jacob found out what it felt like to be cheated by someone.

Jacob got out his best clothes for the occasion and everybody got dressed up. It was going to be a wonderful celebration. Jacob said he would care for Rachel and never let her down, and everybody cheered. The trouble was that, when the bride took off her veil, it wasn't Rachel at all – it was

Leah! Well, Jacob was really angry. 'What do you think you're doing?' he shouted at Laban. 'Seven years I've worked to marry Rachel, and now you've given me the wrong one!'

Leah wasn't very pleased at being called 'the wrong one', but before she could get a word in, Laban answered Jacob. 'I'm sorry,' he said, 'but I had to do it. In these parts, the older daughter has to get married first. But I'll tell you what: if you promise to work another seven years for me, I'll let you marry Rachel next week.'

Jacob nearly said, 'I've already worked for seven years, and you've swindled me.' But he loved Rachel so much that he stopped himself and just said, 'All right, then. I'll work for you for seven years – but I'm going to marry Rachel next week.'

So the next week, they had another big wedding and Jacob married Rachel. And do you know, he kept his word to Laban and worked the whole seven extra years, because he loved Rachel so much that he said she was worth every day of it!

Ain't love grand?

Based on Genesis 29:15-30

Let's Chat

Have you done something today that has shown
how much you love somebody? Sometimes, we do big,
difficult things, like digging someone's garden;
but more often, little things, like smiling, or hugging.
(Why not do that now?)

We're Glad

Let's say 'Thank you' to God
for the things that are special to us
(especially . . .)
Loving God, we like being loved.
We like loving others as well,
and we like to show it.
Thank you for giving us friends,
Thank you especially for . . .
and thank you for each other.

We're Sad

We're sorry, God, for the things we didn't do,
when we could;
for the bad things we've done,
when we didn't need to.
Thank you for loving us,
even when we don't show
that we love each other.

Let's Pray for People

Loving God, some people think no-one loves them.
They don't get much help,
or many hugs, or even smiles.
We know that you love them;
help them to know that too,
and help us to show them
that we love them as well.

NOT A LOT OF BROTHERLY LOVE

J oseph was one of a large family. He had eleven brothers. Can you imagine that! I wonder whether they had trouble remembering each other's names. I bet they did! Anyway, I'm not going to tell you all of them, or you'll be as confused as they probably were!* Now I'd like to tell you what a wonderful boy Joseph was, and how much his brothers loved him, and how much they cared for him. I'd like to. But I can't. The truth is that he was not really a very nice person at all when he was young, although he got better as he got older. When he was a boy, he was always telling tales about his brothers, to get them into trouble – and his father believed him. Now his father should have known better, because he was Jacob, and he'd been no angel when he was Joseph's age. So he should have been wiser than to believe what Joseph was saying. Anyway, Joseph's brothers gradually got more and more fed up with the trouble Joseph caused. Then, one day, they decided they'd had enough.

'He got me into trouble again today,' said Reuben, 'saying I'd neglected the sheep; and I hadn't – I never let them out of my sight.'

'Well,' said Levi, who was older than Joseph but younger than Reuben, 'it wouldn't be so bad if he did any work himself, but he doesn't.' 'That's right,' said Dan, 'and Dad's bought him a new coat. It's got long sleeves! He can't work in that, can he?'

'That's nothing,' said Reuben. 'what about all these dreams he's been telling us about – dreaming that he's the greatest and we're all going to bow and scrape to him? I'm the eldest, and I'll tell you this: I bow and scrape to nobody!'

They decided they'd have to do something to teach Joseph a lesson. Then, one day, they had to take the sheep a long way from the house, looking for some grass. While they were there, they jumped on Joseph and were going to kill him. Reuben

*Just in case your children are so inquisitive that they won't sleep unless you tell them, the names are: Reuben, Simeon, Levi, Judah, Issachar, Zebulun, Benjamin, Dan, Naphtali, Gad and Asher. And if that doesn't put the children to sleep, then you've got real problems!

was very worried. 'Joseph might be a stuck-up little so-and-so,' he thought, 'but he's still our brother.' So he said to the others, 'Don't kill him – just put him into one of these dried-up wells and give him a scare.' He thought he could go back later and rescue Joseph. So that's what they did. Can you imagine how Joseph felt, being left in a deep hole in the ground? He wasn't tough and brave, like his brothers, because he'd been spoilt all his life. So he was really frightened and angry. 'You come and get me out of here,' he kept shouting out and, 'You just wait until I tell Dad what you've done!'

'I've had enough of this,' said one of the bothers, 'the very next camel that comes along, he's on it. I don't care where it's going.' Very soon, they saw some Egyptian traders coming across the desert on camels. They ran and got Joseph out of the hole and took him to meet them. 'Look,' they said, 'we've got something for you – a slave. Thirty pounds and he's yours.' The trader, whose name was Abdul, and who wasn't a very nice man at all, said, 'You must be joking – he doesn't look as if he could survive a good day's work. Thirty pounds indeed. I'll take him off your hands for ten!' 'Twenty-five,' said Dan. 'No way,' said Abdul, 'twenty pounds, take it or leave it. I can't hang around here all day.'

So Joseph was sold for twenty pounds to an Egyptian trader and soon disappeared over the horizon. The problem then was, what were his brothers going to tell their father?

'I know,' said Dan, 'let's say a wolf got him.' And do you know – that is just what they did. Jacob was terribly upset, because he thought he would never see his favourite son again.

But of course, he was wrong.

Joseph, as we know, was still alive, although very frightened. But what no-one knew at that time was that he was going to have great adventures in Egypt and become a very important person.

But I'll have to tell you about that another time.

Based on Genesis 37:1-28

Let's Chat

Talk about what you have done together – *games, outings, etc.*

We're Glad

Dear God,
thank you for . . . *brother/sister/friends*
thank you for the things we do together.
Thank you for the fun we have,
for the games we play,
and especially for . . .

We're Sad

Loving God,
some people don't like us,
and sometimes we don't like them.
We get unhappy,
cross,
selfish,
but you still love us.
Thank you for loving us,
and please help us to love one another.

Let's Pray for People

Let's pray for people we don't see very often.
Thank you, God, for . . .
and for . . .
Keep them safe,
and let them know
that we love them.

JOSEPH'S ADVENTURES

J oseph was taken to Egypt and sold as a slave. But it wasn't very long before he was in trouble again and he finished up in prison. It wasn't really his fault – someone just didn't like him very much and told lies about him. That's what he used to do about his brothers and he learnt that it wasn't funny when it happened to him! But it was while he was in prison that his adventures started.

While Joseph was in prison, Anthony, the palace barman got put in there as well. 'What have you done?' asked Joseph. 'Mind your own business!' replied Anthony, which wasn't very friendly. 'Perhaps he served the wrong drinks to the king,' thought Joseph, but didn't say it, as Anthony was rather a big man and Joseph had learnt not to upset people if he could help it. But next morning, Anthony was very quiet and thoughtful. 'What's the matter?' asked Joseph, and thought he might get told to mind his own business again. But Anthony was much more polite. 'I've had a funny dream,' he said, 'and I don't know what it means.' 'Tell me about it,' suggested Joseph.

'Well,' said Anthony, 'I was standing beside this grapevine and it had three branches. While I was there, the branches grew leaves and then grapes appeared on them.' 'What did you do?' asked Joseph. 'I did what I'm here to do,' replied Anthony, 'I squeezed the juice from the grapes, and made a cup of wine for the king.' 'Well, that's easy to understand,' said Joseph. 'In your dream, each branch is like one day. So you'll be out of here and back in your old job in three days.'

Anthony couldn't believe it when what Joseph said came true! Of course, he could have told the king and perhaps got Joseph released, but he forgot all about it. He was not really very grateful, at all.

So Joseph stayed in prison. Then, two years later, the king had strange dreams. He told the people in the palace, but no-one could explain them. Then the barman remembered. 'Dear me!' he thought, 'Fancy forgetting that!' So he went to the king and said, 'I'm terribly sorry, but I forgot to tell you –

I had a dream, when I was in prison.' The king got impatient. 'Don't come bothering me with your dreams,' he snapped, 'I'm too worried about my own.' 'That's just it, Your Majesty,' answered Anthony. 'There was a prisoner – Joseph, I think he was called – some foreign chap, anyway, and he told me what the dream meant.' 'Was he right?' asked the king. 'Spot on,' said the barman. 'I think he might be able to help you.' So Joseph was sent for.

'It's like this,' said the king, 'I dreamt that I was standing by the river, when seven fat cows came up from the water and stood on the bank.' Anthony interrupted, 'Er. what kind of cows were they, Your Majesty – were they brown or black?' 'Don't interrupt!' said the king, 'or you'll find yourself back in prison.' 'Well!' thought Anthony, 'I only asked!' But he didn't say it. 'As I was saying,' the king went on, 'there were these seven fat cows; then up came seven thin cows and ate all the fat ones! Now what in the world could that mean?'

'That's easy!' said Joseph. 'The cows are like years. There will be seven good years – plenty of food, people will have jobs and no-one will go hungry. But then there'll be seven bad years, without any rain. The crops won't grow, there'll be no water, people will lose their jobs and a lot of people will go hungry. And it will be just as if the seven good years had never happened.'

'That's terrible!' said the king. 'What can we do?' 'You need some help, Your Majesty,' said Joseph. 'Find someone who's really wise and clever, and put him in charge of the country. You've got to save as much as you can in the good years, to see you through the bad.' 'Well,' said the king, 'I can't think of anyone wiser or cleverer than you, so it looks as though you've got the job.'

That was how Joseph became a very important person in Egypt. For the first seven years, he managed all the farms and made sure that as much food as possible was saved. Then, just as he'd said, the bad years came. No food was growing anywhere, not in Egypt and not in the countries round about, either. But no-one starved in Egypt, because Joseph had done his job so well.

Based on Genesis 40-41

Let's Chat

Where have you been today? Have you met anyone new,
or seen anything for the first time?

We're Glad

Wonderful God,
you give us so much.
Thank you for the things we see and hear,
thank you for the people we meet.
Especially . . .

We're Sad

Sometimes, we're so happy
that we don't notice other people
who aren't.
Sometimes, we're so full of ourselves
that we forget to say 'thank you'
We're sorry.
Help us to notice other people,
and to love them.

Let's Pray for People

Let's say 'thank you' to God
for people who've been nice to us today.
Loving God,
We remember . . .
Thank you for *him*.
Thank you for all the things we like about *him*:
(Such as . . .)
Let *him* know how we appreciate *him*.
And help us to show it more ourselves.

BABY IN THE BULRUSHES

A very long time ago, in a place called Egypt, there was a really bad king. He made all the foreign people in his country into slaves. They had to work all day long in the hot sun, making bricks, moving heavy stones about and doing all the jobs that the king didn't want his own people to have to do. Then the king got frightened. He didn't like little boys at all. 'Little boys grow up into men,' he thought, 'and men fight. What if one day they get fed up with being slaves, and attack me?' So he did a horrible thing. He tried to kill all the boy babies.

There was a little girl called Miriam in one of the slave families. She was really pleased because she had a new baby brother. But her parents were very worried, because they knew what the king would do if he found out. 'We can't keep the baby here,' said Mum, 'because they'll come looking for him. What are we going to do?' Miriam had a good idea. 'Let's make a basket from bulrushes,' she said. 'If we tar it well, it will float, and then we can hide it in the rushes at the side of the river.' So that's what they did. They put the little baby boy into the basket and hid it in the bulrushes. 'Miriam,' said Dad, 'you'd better stay here and keep an eye on it, just in case.'

Miriam hid nearby and watched. Imagine how horrified she was when a princess from the king's palace came along to swim in the river! 'Oh dear!' thought Miriam, 'I hope they don't find the baby!' The princess went into the water and began to swim, and then noticed the basket in the reeds. She opened it and cried out, 'Oh what a beautiful baby! But he's crying. He must be frightened, poor little thing!'

'What should I do now?' thought Miriam. 'I know – I'll pretend to be just passing by and see if I can help.' So she strolled along the river bank, humming a little tune to herself, until she accidentally-on-purpose bumped into the princess. 'Ooh! What a lovely baby!' she said, pretending never to have seen him before. 'Yes.' said the princess. 'I think he's a foreign baby.' 'That's torn it!' thought Miriam, 'Now she'll have him

killed.' But the princess was smiling. 'He's such a beautiful baby,' she said, 'and I would love to keep him. So, since no-one knows whose he is, I'll take him back to the palace.'

Then Miriam had a wonderful idea. 'Shall I get you a nurse for him?' she asked, 'After all, you wouldn't want to do everything yourself, Your Highness!' 'What a good idea!' said the princess. 'Go and find a woman from among the foreign slave people, who can nurse him for me.'

Well, Miriam raced home as fast as she could and went bursting into her home, panting for breath. 'Really, Miriam!' said her father, 'How many times must I tell you to be more ladylike? Charging around like that, anyone would think something exciting was happening!' Miriam could hardly talk, she was so out of breath. All she could do was point towards the river, while gasping for air! 'What on earth's the matter?' asked Mum, 'It isn't the baby, is it?' and she began to get very agitated indeed. By now, Miriam was getting her breath back. 'A princess . . .' she spluttered, 'by . . . river . . . found . . . baby . . . needs a nurse.'

When Mum and Dad realised what was going on, they got up and hurried back with Miriam to the river. There they found the princess still holding the baby. Taking a deep breath, Miriam went up to her and said, 'I've found someone who can nurse the baby for you.' 'Good!' smiled the princess, who was nowhere near as horrible as her father, in fact she was rather nice, 'You realise you'll have to live at the palace?' 'Of course,' said Mum. The princess handed over the baby. 'He's a lovely little thing,' she said, 'I wish I knew who his parents are.' Of course, no-one told her, because that would have been too dangerous. But they all set off to the palace together. Miriam was really excited about living in a real palace, with a real live princess – nearly as excited as she was about having a baby brother.

'What are you going to call the baby?' she asked.

'I think I'll call him Moses,' answered the princess.

So the baby was taken to the palace, along with the 'nurse' who was really his mother, and the princess treated him just like one of the royal family.

Based on Exodus 2:1-10

Let's Chat

Do you like surprises?
Can you remember a really lovely surprise you have had?
Or perhaps you have given someone else a surprise?

We're Glad

Amazing God!
Life can be so exciting!
We never know what might happen!
Sometimes, people are nice to us,
when we don't expect it.
Lovely things happen,
which we haven't planned.
Thank you for a wonderful world,
full of surprises.

We're Sad

We're sorry, God,
for letting people down.
We're sorry for not being
as good as we could be.
Help us to give people nice surprises,
not nasty shocks.

Let's Pray for People

God, our friend,
we pray for happy people
(especially . . .)
Thank you for their happiness.
Help us to show them
that we're happy, too.
And we pray for unhappy people
(especially . . .)
Let them know that we care,
and that we're sad for them.

ESCAPING THROUGH THE SEA

M oses grew up in the princess's palace in Egypt, but he had always felt a little different. He never liked the way the wicked king hurt the foreign slaves and one day, after a lot of arguments with the king, he led all the slaves, who were really Israelites, out into the desert to find a new home.

'Where are we going?' they asked. 'I'm not really sure,' said Moses, 'but God has told me it's a wonderful place. There's plenty of food there and lots of milk and honey. And most of all, you'll be free!'

Among the people was a trouble-maker called Simon. He'd never really liked Moses and he certainly didn't like the desert. He thought he would stir up a bit of bother. 'Big deal!' he said, 'I don't see any sign of that here – there's nothing but sand, heat and flies! What have you brought us out here for? We might have been slaves in Egypt, but at least we got fed!'

Then everyone else started complaining, too. They'd already forgotten how dreadful life had been in Egypt!

Meanwhile, back in Egypt, the wicked king was getting complaints from his people, as well. One of his councillors came to see him. His name was Omar and he was a bit like Simon – always wanted to cause trouble if he could.

'Your Majesty,' he said, 'the people aren't happy now that you've let the slaves go. We have to make our own meals, wash our own clothes, clean our own houses . . . and my garden's full of weeds – who's going to pull them up, I'd like to know!' Before long, lots of people joined in, all shouting at the king and demanding the slaves back. Well, the king liked a quiet life – so he sent the army out into the desert to bring the slaves home.

The Israelites were camped at the shore of the Reed Sea. (Most people think it was the Red Sea, but you know better now, don't you?) 'Well,' said Simon, 'another fine mess you've got us into! We can't get across, and it's an awfully long way round.' 'Don't worry,' said Moses, 'God will get us across.' 'Well he'd better hurry,' said Simon, 'because there's a cloud of dust back there, and it looks as if the Egyptians are coming after us.'

'Oh, don't worry about them,' said Moses, 'God will take care of them.'

Then God said a strange thing. 'Don't come crying to me,' he said, 'but tell the people to move forward,' which was a funny thing to say, because that meant walking right into the sea. Well, they dithered about, trying to decide who should go first. Eventually, Moses reached out his hand over the sea and the most amazing thing happened. The sea separated, to the left and right, and there was a pathway of dry land straight through the middle of it. 'That's it!' shouted Moses, 'Now let's go!' Simon still wasn't convinced. 'That's an awful lot of water piled up at each side,' he said, 'and how do we know it won't come down on us?' But he either had to trust God or sit and wait to be captured by the Egyptians. So he decided to risk it.

27

Anyway, by that time, the others were on their way. Down to the sea bed they went, with their donkeys, their carts, and everything they had. As they walked along they could see the water on either side of them and hear the great wind blowing, keeping it apart. 'If that wind drops, we're fish-food,' said Simon, gloomily. 'Well you'd better keep going then!' said his wife, Debbie, who was fed up to the back teeth with Simon's moaning and trouble-making. Well, it seemed like ages they were down on the sea bed, but eventually they started walking uphill and knew they were near the opposite shore. When they got there, Simon still wasn't satisfied. 'If we can do that,' he said, 'so can the Egyptians!' 'The difference is,' said Moses, 'that they haven't got God on their side.' With that, he stretched out his hand again and the wind stopped. The water came rushing back together again, splashing all over the place, with great waves leaping up as the two walls of water met. The noise was deafening! But even louder than the noise of the water was the sound of singing. The Israelite people were celebrating, because now they knew that God really was going to lead them to their promised land.

Based on Exodus 14

Let's Chat

Can you remember going on a journey – perhaps on holiday?
Can you remember the excitement?
Did you see anything new, on the way?

We're Glad

Let's say 'thank you' to God
for this big and exciting world
Loving God,
thank you for showing us new things.
Whenever we start to think
that we know everything,
you show us something new!
Thank you for helping us to learn.

We're Sad

God, forgive us
for not trusting you,
and for not trusting each other.
We don't know very much
about the world,
and we make lots of mistakes.
Help us to trust you more.

Let's Pray for People

Creator God,
you made the world
for us to enjoy.
We pray for people who are unhappy.
Perhaps they think no-one cares.
Help us to show them that we do,
and help them to learn again
what a wonderful world this is.

THE WALLS CAME TUMBLING DOWN

J oshua wasn't happy. 'I wish,' he said, 'that Moses had never passed this job on to me! Being the leader of the Israelites is not easy!'

Joshua had taken over as leader when Moses died. Now he faced a real problem. Between his people and their new home stood a big city called Jericho; and around Jericho were some very high walls. Meanwhile, the people in the city had seen the Israelites coming; and a soldier called Seth was giving orders. 'Hurry up and get those gates shut,' he shouted, 'or they'll be marching in here. That's better – now pile everything you can get up against them.' Before long, the gate couldn't be seen from the inside, completely hidden behind an enormous pile of tables, benches, boxes, rocks and all kinds of other things. Someone had even brought a baby's cradle! 'There!' said Seth, 'That should keep them out!'

What Seth didn't know was that Joshua wasn't going to attack the gates. God had better ideas. 'Don't worry about the gates,' he told Joshua, 'you're going to bring down the walls!' Joshua could hardly believe his ears. 'Those walls must be ten feet thick!' he said. 'What's the matter,' asked God, 'haven't you ever heard of vibration? March the people round the walls every day for a week and, at the end of it, you'll be able to shake the walls down by shouting.'

Well! Can you imagine the sight? Round and round they went, with soldiers in the front blowing their trumpets as loudly as they could. The enemy soldiers on top of the walls thought it was a great joke. Before long, they were selling tickets and people were queuing up to buy them. 'Come and see the silly Israelites walking round the wall!' shouted Seth, and every day more people came to watch. The Israelite people didn't like the job much – people shouted insults at them and dropped rubbish from the walls – but Joshua made them carry on going round. Then at last, after a week, he shouted, 'All right, let them have it!' And what do you think they did?

They shouted.

Yes, honestly! Everyone who wasn't already blowing a trumpet shouted as loudly as possible. At the same time they kept on tramping round the walls. You never heard a noise like it. The air shook with the noise, and the ground shook with the tramping of feet, and the people watching thought it was great fun – until the walls began to shake as well. It was only a little at first – just a kind of gentle trembling. But it grew, and the walls shook more and more as the shouting got louder. The watching people started to panic and to try to get down from the walls. Everybody was running and shouting.

Seth was trying to tell people not to panic, but the more he shouted the more they panicked! Then, gradually, cracks started to appear in the walls. The cracks got bigger and the walls began to sway, and then there was a great CRRRRRASH! The walls had fallen down.

31

The Israelites could hardly believe what had happened. 'All we did was shout,' someone said, 'and the walls just came tumbling down!'

'Well, there you are,' smiled Joshua, 'it's amazing how much damage a bit of noise can do!'

Based on Joshua 6

Let's Chat

Do you like music? What kind? Or perhaps you just enjoy
making a noise! Do you get told off for being too noisy?
Sometimes, noise is bad, but not always – think of fire alarms,
people shouting warnings etc.

We're Glad

Creator God,
thank you for music,
for singing;
thank you for making us able to talk,
and to hear.
But thank you for quietness, too,
and help us to know
when to sing and shout,
and when to be quiet.

We're Sad

Let's say 'sorry' to God
for the times we've upset people
by being too noisy.
We're sorry, God, for being thoughtless.
We don't mean to upset others,
but sometimes we're so busy enjoying ourselves
that we forget them.
Help us to remember other people.

Let's Pray for People

Loving God,
we pray for people who can't speak,
and for people who can't hear, (especially . . .)
Help them to find other ways
of enjoying your world, and having fun.
And please help us to remember them,
and not to let them be left out.

ANOTHER LOVE STORY

T his is the story of Ruth. Ruth was very happy with her husband, Chilion, and together they looked after his mother, Naomi, whose husband had died. They were very happy together, but then something dreadful happened: Chilion died as well. In those days, there were not many jobs for women, which meant that without husbands they would find life very hard. So Naomi said to Ruth, 'You must go and find another husband – don't worry about me.' But Ruth was worried – very worried indeed. 'What will you do?' she asked, 'How will you live?' 'You mustn't worry about that,' said Naomi, 'you are young and beautiful, and if you are on your own you will find a husband, but not as long as you have an old lady living with you.'

It was true that Ruth was young and beautiful, and she certainly would have plenty of young men wanting to marry her. But she couldn't leave Naomi. 'Whatever happens,' she said, 'we'll face it together – but I'm not leaving you on your own.' Naomi thought how lucky she was to have a daughter-in-law like Ruth. 'Well,' she said, 'I hear they've had a good harvest in my home town. Perhaps we should go back there and see what we can do.' So Ruth and Naomi set out for Naomi's home town, which was Bethlehem. (Have you heard of that before, somewhere?)

When they got to Bethlehem, Naomi's family were really glad to see her, but sad that her husband had died and she was now so poor.

Now, Naomi had a relative in Bethlehem who was very rich and, as well as being rich, he was very kind (which was lucky, because not all rich people are). Ruth got a job, working in the field for Boaz. She went behind the people who were picking the corn and collected up any bits that they dropped. Naomi told Boaz all about how kind Ruth had been to her. 'I kept telling her to leave me and take care of herself,' Naomi said, 'but all she would say was, "Whatever comes, we'll face it together".' 'She's obviously a very special kind of person,' said Boaz, 'everyone's talking about how hard she works. I must try to find a way of repaying her.' So the next day, Boaz spoke to the workers. 'Drop a little extra corn,' he said, 'and let Ruth pick it up. Oh, and if I hear of anyone giving her any trouble, they'll be sorry. Got it?' 'Got it, boss!' the workers chorused. 'Good!' said Boaz. 'Now get back to work.'

While Ruth was working, Boaz came and asked her how she was getting on. 'And what are you doing for lunch?' he asked her. 'Oh, don't worry about me,' said Ruth, 'I've brought some bread and some fruit with me. I'll just go and sit under the cedar tree to eat it.' 'Well,' said Boaz, 'I'd be very happy if you'd come and have lunch with me.' Ruth was really pleased about that, and from then on she joined Boaz

for lunch every day. They spent a lot of time together and they soon began to realise that they were not 'just good friends', any more! Then, one day, Boaz plucked up the courage to ask Ruth to marry him. Of course, she said 'Yes!' because Boaz was a good and kind man, and Ruth had come to love him very much indeed. It was a wonderful wedding.

All the other farm workers came, along with the bride's and bridegroom's friends and, of course, Naomi had pride of place among them. Ruth looked absolutely beautiful, and Boaz looked pretty good too, in his best clothes. Everyone had a wonderful time – they sang and danced and kept on drinking a toast, 'to life!' After it was all over, Ruth and Boaz went and settled down to begin their life together in his house. Before long, they had some good news for everyone. Ruth was going to have a baby. Well, of course, there was more singing, more dancing, more shouts of 'to life!' Everyone was happy, and no-one more so than Ruth and Boaz. There again, perhaps there was one other person who was at least as happy as they were. Can you guess who that was?

Of course, it was Naomi. She was so happy she could hardly stand still – because she was going to be a grandma!

Based on the Book of Ruth

Let's Chat

Friends. Think about neighbours, people at school – you may
be surprised at how many friends you've got!

We're Glad

God, our friend,
thank you for the friends you give us.
Sometimes we need them very much,
and it's good to know
they won't let us down.
Thank you for being our best friend,
the one we know we can trust,
even more than the others.

We're Sad

Loving God, we're sorry
for letting people down,
and for letting you down.
Make us more loving,
more careful,
more like you.

Let's Pray for People

Caring God,
we trust you,
and we trust each other.
We know there are people who are frightened,
who think they have no friends,
who dare not trust anybody
because they've been let down.
Help them to find friends,
and help them to trust you.

BIGGEST ISN'T ALWAYS BEST

G oliath had always been a bully. When he was a child, he used to take all the other children's toys. No-one tried to stop him because he was so big, and they were all afraid of him. It wasn't that he really wanted the toys – he just wanted to show how big and tough he was. His parents used to worry a lot. 'What sort of person is he going to be?' they wondered. They were afraid he might get into trouble. When he said he was going to join the army, his father said, 'That will make a man of him. He'll learn to do as he's told and be polite to the people in charge.'

Then the army Goliath was in, the Philistines, went to war against the Israelites; but the Israelites didn't have anyone as big as Goliath, and everyone who tried to fight him got killed. Goliath used to enjoy showing off. Every morning, he went to the top of a hill and shouted across to the Israelites.

'Send someone to fight me,' he shouted, 'if you can find anyone big enough. If he beats me, you can have all the Philistine land, and we'll be your slaves. Of course, if I win, the Philistines get all *your* land, and *you* become *our* slaves. Well, come on then,' he shouted, 'who's going to fight me?'

It was just like when he was at school – everyone was afraid of him, and he loved it!

One morning, while he was shouting insults at the Israelites, a shepherd boy called David came to the Israelites' camp. He'd only really come to bring his brothers some food. They were all in the army, but David was very small – about a metre and a half in his sandals – and after all, someone had to mind the sheep, so he'd never been a soldier. But when he heard Goliath shouting, he thought, 'Someone ought to teach that big bully a lesson!' He went to the King and said, 'I'll fight Goliath for you.'

Well, King Saul had never heard anything so funny! 'Oh yes,' he mocked, 'and what are you going to do – hit him in the kneecaps? Ho, ho, ho!' Well, it was true that David certainly was very small, compared with Goliath. But his father, Jesse, had always told his sons, 'Biggest isn't always best.' So David thought he could have a go at fighting Goliath. 'I'm a shepherd,' he said, 'and when lions and wolves attack the sheep, I drive them away. If God can help me fight a lion, he can certainly help me with Goliath.'

'Well, said the king, 'you'd better borrow my armour to protect you. Come and try it on.'

Have you ever tried on a grown-up's clothes? Well, you can imagine how silly David looked and felt in the big man's armour. Of course, it wasn't only too big, it was too heavy as well. David tried to walk around in it and people couldn't help laughing at him. When he tried to get the sword out and wave it, they all threw themselves about and roared with laughter. 'I'll make you sorry you laughed at me,' said David, as he took off the armour and marched out.

David went down to the stream and chose five smooth stones for ammunition, then he went out to meet Goliath. 'Now what have we here?' bellowed the giant, 'Are you the best that feeble lot could find. I'll feed you to the birds – I'll give you to the vultures for food – I'll . . .' 'Oh no you won't,' replied David, 'because God's going to help me.' At that, the giant lost his temper and aimed his spear at David. Quick as a flash, David put a stone into his sling, swung it round a few times and let go. The stone flew through the air and hit the giant, bang in the middle of his forehead. He stopped for a moment, dropped his spear and sword, and then swayed a few times, before falling to the earth with a terrific crash. The ground shook so hard that people who weren't watching thought there'd been an earthquake!

All the Israelite army were very pleased with David, but the Philistines weren't, of course – they got very frightened and ran away. They had learnt the hard way that 'biggest isn't always best'!

Based on 1 Samuel 17

Let's Chat

It's nice to feel important. Some people like to
frighten others, to make themselves feel important.
Others want people to love them.
Which is best – fights or cuddles?
(Here's a chance for some fun!)

We're Glad

Heavenly Father,
thank you for our friends,
who play with us, and talk with us,
thank you for people who care for us,
and teach us,
and thank you for the fun we have together.
Thank you for the things we've done well,
with your help.

We're Sad

Sometimes we're not nice to each other.
we get cross, we hurt each other,
we say things we shouldn't,
or sometimes we just don't notice
when someone needs help.
We're sorry,
and we'll try to do better tomorrow.

Let's Pray for People

Loving Father,
it's easy to say that we trust you,
but we still get worried sometimes.
Help anyone who feels frightened tonight,
or who is lonely.

THE FIRST LION TAMER

D aniel lived in a place a long way away, called Babylon. He hadn't been born there, but had come from another country. He was a very wise and clever man who understood things which no-one else did; he even seemed to be able to tell what would happen in the future, and to understand the meaning of people's dreams! Because of this, he'd become very popular with the king, King Darius, who asked his advice and made him a very important person. But not everyone liked him. Some people just can't stand the idea of people from other countries being cleverer than they are – and they certainly don't like taking orders from them!

So, one day, some of the king's advisers got together to think how they could get rid of Daniel. They were a nasty little group of people, who pretended to love the king, but were really only interested in what they could get for themselves. Whenever they got the chance to cheat the king, they did.

One of them, a very unpleasant character called Ned (not at all the sort of person you'd ask to your birthday party), said he had an idea. 'You know,' he said to the others, 'once a law has been made in our country, not even the king can change it. What we have to do is get King Darius to pass a law against praying. Daniel loves praying to his God and we'd be able to get rid of him.'

It was true that Daniel loved to pray. Every day, he set aside a special time for prayer. A lot of people thought that that was why he was so wise and clever, because he spent so much time talking to God.

So, Ned and his friends went to see King Darius. When they got there, they weren't sure who should do the talking. They whispered among themselves and tried to push each other forward (rather the way children sometimes do) and eventually Ned found himself standing in front of the king. King Darius was getting a bit impatient by now. 'Well?' he asked, 'What do you want?

'Your Majesty,' said Ned, 'we think you should pass a law against praying – except to you, of course. People should not be allowed to pray to whatever God they like.'

King Darius thought that sounded like a good idea – and he was very pleased to think of everyone worshipping him! So he made the new law. What should be the punishment for breaking it? 'How about being fed to the lions?' suggested Ned, 'That should put them off.' And secretly, he thought, 'and it should get rid of Daniel once and for all, as well!'

Next day, when Daniel got ready to pray, Ned and his horrible friends were waiting. They rushed into his house, arrested him, and took him to the king. 'Oh dear,' thought King Darius, 'I never expected this! Daniel's a nice fellow – and very useful, too. What am I going to do?' Of course, there wasn't anything he could do. He couldn't change the law. Daniel had to be put in the lions' den.

Can you imagine being trapped with half a dozen hungry lions? Daniel must have been scared, even though he trusted God! King Darius wasn't very happy either! He didn't get a wink of sleep all night, worrying about Daniel. In the morning, he got up and rushed to the lions' den. He didn't really expect to find Daniel alive, but he had to go on hoping. Imagine his surprise when he called out to Daniel and Daniel answered! He got the keepers to open the door, and there was Daniel, sitting among the lions and stroking them as though they were kittens!

King Darius decided he was going to do something new – he changed the law! He made Daniel his closest friend and he sent for Ned and his little group.

'Well,' he said, 'you wanted Daniel to be put in with the lions and I did that. Here he is, still among us. So now it's your turn. Let's see how you get on with them.'

Can you imagine what happened when the lions saw Ned? They weren't as nice to him and his friends as they had been to Daniel – which is why it's still a good idea to stay at a safe distance from lions, however good or bad you think you are!

Then King Darius did a very adventurous thing. He actually changed the law. 'It's about time,' he said to Daniel, 'that people stopped worshipping me, as though I was a god and started worshipping the real God instead.'

And that was exactly what happened.

Based on Daniel 6

Let's Chat

Do you enjoy prayer time? Can you imagine somebody
telling you that you weren't allowed to do it any more?
How would you feel?

We're Glad

Loving God,
we like talking to you,
thank you for asking us to pray,
thank you for listening,
thank you that no-one tries to stop us.
Amen.

We're Sad

Heavenly Father,
it's easy to forget about you,
and not listen to you.
We could talk to you more often,
but we forget,
or sometimes it's just that
we'd rather do something else.
We're sorry.

Let's Pray for People

We pray for people who can't pray themselves.
maybe they're too frightened,
maybe they don't know the words,
maybe they just don't know you.
Help them to know you,
to love you,
and to pray to you.
And help us to remember
to pray for them.
Amen.

HAVING A WHALE OF A TIME

J onah was a fairly ordinary sort of chap really, rather like people we know, except that he lived a very long time ago, and a very long way away from here, in Israel. He enjoyed looking after his garden, and chatting with his neighbours but, like many other people then and now, there was something about him that really was not very nice. And we'll see what that was in a minute.

Jonah had often thought that he'd like to do something really special for God, and he used to day-dream about the brave things he might do – rescuing people from torture, or saving someone who was drowning, or perhaps stopping a robbery. Other times, he would dream about becoming a doctor, or a great lawyer . . .

But God had a different idea. That's the thing about God – just when we think we've worked out what we'd like to do for him, he thinks of something different! So he told Jonah to go to Nineveh, a very large town, and give them a message. The people in Nineveh were living very badly. They were lying, they were stealing, they were fighting with one another – in fact Nineveh was not a good place to be at all. So the message Jonah had to give them was that they had to change and start being good to one another, because if they went on like that, they would all end up being killed.

You might expect Jonah to be pleased that God had such an important job for him – but he wasn't. As I told you, Jonah was really quite an ordinary, and rather nice person, but he had one very bad point indeed. 'Why should I go to Nineveh?' he thought. 'It's not in this country. All the people there are foreigners – why should I help them?'

That was Jonah's bad point – he thought that anybody who was from another country was bad, and he only wanted to help his own people. 'After all,' he thought, 'there are plenty of people here who lie and steal and fight. I should really go to them, not some foreign place. When all's said and done, charity begins at home!' But he knew it was no good arguing with God, who had quite made up his mind that

Jonah was to go to Nineveh.

The more Jonah thought about it, the less he wanted to go. 'I know,' he thought, 'I'll run away to Spain, and hide from God.' So he went down to the docks at a place called Joppa, and said to the man in the ticket office, 'I'd like to go to Spain, please.' The man took Jonah's money, handed him a ticket and pointed to a ship. 'There you are,' he said, 'take the third ship along.'

Jonah boarded the ship and settled down for a long cruise, wondering whether God had noticed yet, that he'd run away. Poor old Jonah didn't understand that you can't run away from God – but he was about to find out! They hadn't been at sea very long when the most horrible storm began. The wind and waves were throwing the little ship about on the sea, while the thunder and lightning was frightening everyone, even the really tough sailors! They were all wondering what they ought to do, and Jonah was getting more and more frightened because he knew! After a little while, he did a very brave thing. He went to the captain and said, 'It's all my fault. I'm running away from God, and as long as I'm here, this storm's going to go on. I-I-I think you'd better th-th-throw me overboard.'

'Good grief!' said the captain, 'We can't do that! What would your God do to us if we did a thing like that?' But the storm got even worse, and the sailors got even more frightened, and eventually they decided to do what Jonah said. So over the side he went, with all the sailors praying like mad, asking God not to be angry! As soon as Jonah hit the water, the storm stopped. All the sailors were very pleased – but what about Jonah?

God hadn't forgotten Jonah, and he sent a very big fish, which opened its mouth and swallowed Jonah whole – which was a good thing, really! Imagine Jonah's surprise, when he looked around! 'Well!' he thought, 'I wonder how I get out of here.' But he couldn't think of a way that he really fancied very much, so he decided to sit and wait. Three days he was there. Can you imagine being shut up in a stuffy, smelly place for three whole days and nights? Still, it gave him a bit of time to think and, although he still didn't like the idea of being nice to 'foreigners', he realised that running away from God was rather silly. So he decided that if he got out of there in one piece, he'd do what God wanted!

When the three days were up, God got the fish to put Jonah back onto dry land – not far from Nineveh. This time, Jonah did what God had wanted. He walked right through the city, telling everyone to change, before it was too late. And the amazing thing is that they listened to him. They stopped lying, and cheating, and fighting, and life became very good indeed.

Jonah wasn't very pleased about that, because he still didn't like the people he called 'foreigners'. But the strange thing was that the person whom that made unhappy was Jonah himself.

Isn't that a shame?

Based on the Book of Jonah

Let's Chat

Who have you met today? People you like? Some that you
don't? What have you done? Have you enjoyed everything,
or were there things you'd rather have got out of?

We're Glad

Heavenly Father,
thank you for today:
thank you for the people we've met,
thank you for the things we've done.
Thank you for the things we've enjoyed,
and thank you for being there,
and helping us,
at other times.

We're Sad

We would like to be friends with everybody,
but it's hard.
Some people are not easy to like.
There again, we're sometimes difficult to like, as well!
But you still love us.
We're sorry we don't love people the way you do.
Forgive us,
and help us to do better.

Let's Pray for People

Loving God, you love everybody.
You love us,
when we don't deserve it.
Bless those people we don't like,
and show us what is good about them.

No Room

S| imon and Susannah ran the local bed-and-breakfast in Bethlehem. It wasn't a very grand place – just an ordinary house with a few extra rooms built on, and a stable at the back where guests could leave their donkeys or camels. Simon and Susannah had worked very hard to make it into the kind of place where people would enjoy spending a few nights. They always made sure that the rooms were clean, with a large jug of water in each room for washing and another one for drinking. So their guests were very well looked after.

It wasn't just business – Simon and Susannah really cared about their visitors, and wanted them to be happy. They were very kind people, and Simon certainly never meant to be unkind, but sometimes he did hurtful things without meaning to – and this was one of them. So, not for the first time, he was getting a good telling off from Susannah.

'D'you mean to tell me that you turned that poor young couple away, on a night like this,' Susannah shouted at him, 'and her expecting a baby at any minute?' 'But, my love, we haven't any room,' said Simon, 'what else was I to do?' It was true that there wasn't any room in the house. People were sleeping in the passage-ways, and just about everywhere you could think of. In fact, there were even guests sleeping on the dining room floor. They had to be woken first each morning, so that they could get dressed before the other guests came down for breakfast. So you might think that Simon had been quite right in sending some people away. But Susannah was still angry.

'Where there's a will, there's a way,' she said. 'I'm going to get that couple back here, and by the time I do, you'd better have thought of something.' With that, she went out into the cold night, leaving Simon scratching his head. Suddenly, he had an idea.

Meanwhile, Susannah was searching all over town. It wasn't easy, because the streets were crowded – people on donkeys, people walking, people carrying babies, some with small children who didn't want to go where their parents were going, and said so. One little boy caused a real fuss when he sat down in the road and refused to move, with all the other people shouting at him to get out of the way. Susannah would have stopped to help, but she had to keep looking for the couple. Eventually, she saw them. She recognised the man straight away – tall, handsome, and worried-looking!

The couple, who turned out to be called Mary and Joseph, were very pleased to see Susannah. They had been getting very worried, because it seemed as though Mary was about to have her baby any minute! 'Don't worry,' said Susannah, 'I'm afraid that husband of mine is a bit silly sometimes, but he means well.' 'We don't want to be any trouble,' said Joseph,' but we really do need to find somewhere very soon.' 'No trouble at all,' said Susannah. 'You come with me, and if Simon hasn't thought of something by now, he'll be sorry!' So Susannah took them back to the house.

When they arrived, Simon was looking very pleased with himself. 'I still haven't got a room,' he said, 'but there's a shed out the back – not much in it, just a cow and a couple of goats, so it smells a bit, but there's plenty of straw, and anyway, it's all there is.'

'It will have to do,' said Joseph, 'we're far too tired to go on looking.' So he gathered some straw together for Mary to lie on. Mind you, she didn't get a lot of sleep. Just as they had expected, their baby son, Jesus, was born that night. Susannah was wonderfully helpful and stayed with Mary all night to help her. Simon was quite excited, too. He kept coming and knocking on the stable door, calling out, 'Has the baby arrived yet?' When Jesus was born, they realised there was nowhere to put him, where he could sleep. Then Susannah had an idea. 'I know,' she said, 'we could put some clean straw in that feeding trough the animals are using.' So she went and pushed the animals out of the way, emptied the trough and put clean hay in it. Then, she wrapped the baby Jesus in strips of cloth to keep him warm, and put him in the trough. The animals weren't happy. They kept trying to get close to the manger. No-one was sure whether they were trying to see the baby or eat the straw! Eventually, Joseph tied them up to some hooks in the wall, and gave them some piles of hay to eat. 'There,' he said, 'that should keep them happy for a while.'

Suddenly, the shed seemed a lot nicer than it had before. Joseph and Mary had their new baby, and they were very glad indeed that they'd found somewhere in time!

Based on Luke 2:1-7

Let's Chat

Look around the room. This is home! What is special about
it? (*decor, personal belongings, holiday souvenirs, etc.*)
Who lives in it? Is it warm, safe, etc?

We're Glad

Thank you God,
for our home;
for each other,
for friends.
Thank you for everything
that we share together

We're Sad

This is our home, Jesus,
and we love one another.
It's just that sometimes
we don't show it.
Sometimes we hurt people,
especially people we love.
We're sorry.

Let's Pray For People

Lord Jesus,
we pray for people who have no home,
who have no safe place to sleep;
people who don't feel loved
the way we do.
You know what it's like, Jesus.
Help us all to love one another
and make happy homes.
Amen.

NEVER MIND THE SHEEP, LOOK FOR THE BABY

J ed and Enoch were shepherds, and Jed was rather a grumpy one – at least on this particular night. 'It's no good,' he moaned, 'we've got to get out of this business.' 'Oh yes?' replied Enoch, 'And what would you do instead?' That was the question. Jed really wanted some glamour, some excitement in his life. He would probably have wanted to be a film star, or a stunt-man, if films had been invented then, but they hadn't. 'I don't know what I want to do,' he snapped, 'all I know is, I don't want to do this! All we do is sit out here all night, watching sheep. Nothing ever happens. It must be three weeks since we last had to chase a wolf away! We can't even go into the town for a drink, because the people all tell us to go away.' 'Well,' said Enoch, 'you must admit that this isn't the cleanest job in the world.' Jed was about to make a rather rude reply when he noticed something strange. The sky was getting light. 'Wow!' he said, 'The night went quickly.' But Enoch knew better. 'That's not the dawn,' he said, 'there's something funny going on.'

What happened next made Jed wish he'd kept his big mouth shut about being bored! There before his very eyes, stood an angel. Well, I say *stood* but *hovered* might be a better word, because he didn't seem to have his feet on the ground. In fact it was difficult to say exactly whether he was on the ground, or in the sky – he was just, sort of, *there*! He was dressed in a white robe, which shone so brightly that Jed thought the sun itself had come to life! Even Enoch was a bit flustered. 'Wh-wh-what d'you think we ought to do?' he asked Jed. Well! Talk about a silly question! 'Run like mad!' said Jed, 'What else!' Then the angel spoke. 'Now, don't be silly,' he said, 'I'm not going to hurt you. All I want to do is give you a message.' 'A-a m-message?' stammered Jed. 'That's right,' said the angel, 'great news – about a special baby who's been born in Bethlehem. His name is Jesus, and he's going to save the world.'

By now, Jed was really thinking this was a nightmare and had almost decided that a boring job like shepherding was

just what he really wanted! 'I'll tell you what,' said the angel, 'this will prove it to you. Go to Bethlehem and look for a baby, wrapped in swaddling clothes, and lying in a cattle feeding trough.' Enoch was about to ask, '*Whereabouts* in Bethlehem?' when he suddenly heard Jed gasp, 'Goodness me, there's thousands of them!' The sky was full of angels, all singing and dancing and having a real whoopee of a time! 'Glory to God!' they were singing, 'Peace on earth!' The whole sky was lit up like Corinth (which was the nearest thing they had to Blackpool in those parts) and it sounded as though all the choirs in the world had got together with a big amplifier! Then, all of a sudden, they'd gone! Just like that! The field was dark again, just as it had been before.

Enoch sat there for a time, rubbing his eyes and saying, 'It must had been a dream!' over and over again.

'What must have been a dream?' asked Jed. 'I saw an angel!' said Enoch. 'Well if that was a dream, we must both have had the same one together,' said Jed. 'Anyway, there's only one way to find out. We've got to go to Bethlehem.' 'We can't do that,' Enoch protested, 'who'll look after the sheep?' 'Never mind the sheep!' exclaimed Jed, 'We've got to look for the baby!' Jed was getting impatient. After all this time, and after all his complaining, something exciting was happening and all Enoch could think about was counting sheep!

So they set off for the town, with Jed rushing on ahead and Enoch following behind. When they got there, they knocked on the door of the first guest house they came to. 'Er, excuse me,' Enoch asked the innkeeper, 'we're looking for a new-born baby in a feeding trough.' 'You're drunk!' said the innkeeper, and slammed the door. So they moved on to the next house and Enoch tried again. 'What!' exclaimed the innkeeper, 'Who would put a baby in a feeding trough? This is a respectable inn – we don't do that kind of thing here.' As they walked down the street, Jed heard two people talking. 'That's right,' said one, 'the family are actually living in the stable – new-born baby, and all!' 'Well I never!' said the other, and would have said more but Jed interrupted. 'What did you say?' he asked, 'A family in a stable, with a new baby?' 'Oh yes!' was the reply, 'Over at Simon and Suzannah's place. They hadn't got any rooms left, so they put the family in the stable. That's the place, over there.'

Enoch and Jed were very excited by now. They ran across the street, down the alleyway beside the inn, and there they saw the stable. When they looked inside, they saw a man and a woman, with their little baby. The baby, just as the angel said, was wrapped in swaddling clothes, and lying in the hay in the feeding trough.

The man, Joseph, noticed them and invited them in. 'Look, Mary,' he said to his wife, 'we've got visitors.' Mary was very tired, but she smiled and welcomed the shepherds. 'We've come to see the baby,' said Enoch. 'What's his name?' asked Jed. 'We're going to call him Jesus,' said Mary, 'but do tell me – why have you come to see us?' Jed replied, 'Because an angel appeared, and told us that this baby was very special.' 'That's funny,' said Mary, thoughtfully, 'an angel said the same thing to me. I wonder what he meant.'

'I don't know,' said Joseph, 'but perhaps we'll find out when he grows up.'

Based on Luke 2:8-20

Let's Chat

Can you remember having some exciting news,
or being given a lovely surprise?

We're Glad

Wonderful God,
how you surprise us!
Thank you for doing things we don't expect.
Thank you for being with us,
even when we can't see you.
Thank you for loving us,
even when we're horrible!
Thank you!

We're Sad

We're sorry, God, for ignoring you.
Sometimes we find other things more interesting,
or less difficult,
than doing what you want us to do.
Then we miss out,
and sometimes other people are hurt,
because we didn't pay attention.
We're sorry.

Let's Pray For People

God, our helper,
life can be so exciting,
but it can be so dull, as well!
Help people who are bored, or fed up.
Show them something new,
something exciting, something hopeful.
And show us how we can help, too.

RIDE THAT CAMEL, FOLLOW THAT STAR!

M|elchior, Caspar and Balthazar were three wise men. They used to meet together often to talk about important things and to look at the stars. But they didn't just look at the stars; they actually tried to work out what the different stars and planets were about. They would sit around, very late at night (long after well-behaved children were asleep!) discussing whatever new star they had most recently seen. One evening, Melchior got very excited. 'Look over there!' he shouted to the others. 'There's a great big star that I've never seen before.' 'He's right,' said Caspar, 'I've never seen that one, either. I wonder what it means.' So Balthazar went and got the special books which all wise men in those days read, and looked it up. 'Let me see,' he said, '"Star – extra bright . . ."' then he got really excited. 'It says here,' he told the others, 'that when a special star like that appears, it means an important king has been born.' 'Then what are we waiting for?' said Melchior, 'Let's go and find him.'

Everybody suddenly got very busy. Melchior called his servants, and said, 'Get the camels ready for a long journey. We'll need plenty of food, lots of water, changes of clothes, tents to sleep in – and don't forget the first aid kit.' No-one got any sleep that night and by the next day, they were ready to go. 'Well done, everybody,' said Balthazar, 'now get some rest. We'll have to travel at night, so that we can see the star. That gives you a few hours to sleep.' The servants were very pleased to hear that, because they were extremely tired! So they all went off to bed.

As it began to get dark, the star appeared again. 'Come on everyone,' shouted Balthazar, 'let's get moving!' And so they did. The three wise men went first, on their camels, and behind them came a long train of camels, carrying all the food, water, tents, bedding, and of course not forgetting the first aid kit, and leading the camels were the servants, who were nearly as excited as Melchior, Caspar and Balthazar.

They travelled through the desert for many weeks, moving at night, when they could see the star, and sleeping in their tents during the day, shaded from the hot sun. Sometimes it got very scary, when they could hear wild animals howling, and some of the servants began to get nervous. But eventually, they saw a big city ahead. 'Where are we?' asked Melchior. 'According to my reckoning,' said Caspar, 'that should be Jerusalem.' 'Good,' said Balthazar, 'that's a capital city. All we have to do is find the palace, and we'll have found the king.' So they all agreed that that was what they would do.

Now the king in Jerusalem was the wicked King Herod – and he got a bit worried when he saw the wise men. 'What do you want?' he asked. 'Well, it's like this, Your Majesty,' said Balthazar, 'We've seen a special star, which says that a king is being born, and we've followed it to your city. We've got presents for him, and everything.' 'King?' thought Herod, 'I'm the king! There's not room for another one round here. This is really rather worrying!' Then one of his courtiers whispered to him, 'That sounds like the king the bible speaks of – the great leader promised by God.' 'Over my dead body!' Herod whispered back. 'We'd better find him and get rid of him. Does the bible say where he's going to be born?' 'Yes, your majesty,' answered the courtier, 'In Bethlehem.' 'Right!' whispered Herod, 'Let's leave it to these people to find him for us.' Then he turned back to the wise men, and pretended to smile. 'I think the king you're looking for is in Bethlehem,' he said. 'When you've found him, would you let me know where he is, so that I can take him a present, as well?' Off went the wise men, and Herod turned to his courtiers and said, 'Right! When those silly men come back and tell us where this so-called king is, we'll go and get him. King indeed!'

The wise men went to Bethlehem and when they got there, what do you think they found? There was the star, shining down and showing them exactly where the new king was. So they went in and found Mary and Joseph with Jesus. 'Hello,' said Melchior, 'I hope we're not disturbing you, but we've come a very long way to see you. My name is Melchior and these are my friends, Caspar and Balthazar. We've come all the way across the desert to find your son.' 'Well,' said Mary, 'this is Jesus. He does seem to be causing a lot of excitement. We've had all kinds of visitors.' Melchior went over to Jesus. 'We've brought you some presents,' he said, 'look: gold, for a king.' 'But not just any king,' said Caspar, 'God's very special king. So I've brought some incense.' Then Balthazar said, 'I've brought you some spices. Being a king is hard, and you will have to suffer.'

The wise men were about to go when Joseph said,'You have come a long way. Stay and eat with us.' 'Thank you very much,' said Melchior and over the meal they told Mary and Joseph about their adventures in the desert – about the sandstorms, the heat, the wild animals and about the pranks the servants got up to, burying one another in the sand! 'We've had some adventures here;' said Joseph, 'when we arrived the town was crowded and there was no-where to stay. We ended up using a feeding trough for a cradle!' 'I don't suppose the donkey thought much of that!' laughed Balthazar. 'As a matter of fact, he didn't,' said Mary, 'but things are a little better now.'

After the meal, the wise men went away to their tents to sleep. 'We mustn't forget,' said Melchior, 'to call on that nice King Herod tomorrow, and tell him where Jesus is.' But that night he had a strange dream. An angel came to him and said, 'That "nice King Herod" as you call him is bad news. Whatever you do, don't tell him where the new king is, or there'll really be trouble.' So the next day, as they got ready to leave, Melchior said, 'I've worked out a different way to go home; we're taking the pretty way.' 'What about Herod?' said Balthazar. 'Shifty character,' said Melchior, 'don't trust him a millimetre! I vote we give him a miss.' 'Good idea!' said Caspar, 'Let's go home.'

Based on Matthew 2:1-12

Let's Chat

Do you like journeys – on buses, or trains, or in cars?
Do you like puzzles? Can you remember going on
a special journey, or solving a puzzle?

We're Glad

Dear God,
sometimes we have to make an effort:
search for what we want,
think about things, work things out.
That's why you gave us eyes, and brains.
Help us to use them,
and make us thankful that we've got them.

We're Sad

We're sorry about being lazy.
We're sorry about the things we miss,
that you're trying to show us, or tell us.
We're sorry for the times
when we couldn't be bothered to think,
to try to understand
what you were saying.
Forgive us,
make us more curious, more interested.

Let's Pray For People

Loving God,
we pray for people who are sick,
and can't go out,
people who can't walk very well,
people who can't see and hear
the wonderful things in the world.
Show us if there are ways
we can help them,
so that they will know
what a good world this is.

THE MAN NOBODY WANTED

J|oe was very unhappy. He hadn't got any friends, or a home, or a job. In fact, he hadn't got anything, apart from the clothes he was wearing, and they weren't very nice – well, they wouldn't be, since he never got the chance to change them!

It hadn't always been like that. Joe used to have lots of friends. He had a very nice home, too – his father was a farmer, and Joe used to enjoy life on the farm, watching the crops grow and helping look after the animals. As he grew up, he became quite good-looking – tall and slim, with long dark hair and a very distinguished-looking beard. Everyone liked Joe and he was often invited to parties and dances. But that was before his illness.

Joe developed a very nasty skin disease. No-one's really sure exactly what it was, but it looked horrible! Everyone was afraid that if he came near them, they would catch it from him. So they told him to go away. Grown-ups stopped their children playing with him, and taught them to be afraid of him too. They used to stand a long way away and shout nasty things to him, and if he came a bit too near they would start throwing stones at him. No-one loved him. He was terribly sad.

Even his parents were afraid. 'I'm sorry Joe, but you can't stay here,' his father said, 'we don't want the family going down with it, too, whatever it is. You'll have to go and live in the caves just outside the town.' 'Don't worry,' said his mother, 'we'll see you don't starve. We'll bring you food every day.' So Joe had to leave home and live outside the town, right away from other people. His parents kept their word and took him food, but it wasn't enough. They were afraid to touch him in case they caught his disease. What Joe wanted more than anything else was to be hugged!

Then he heard about a man called Jesus, who could work miracles. 'Well,' he thought, 'if people were nice to me, that would be a miracle!' So, he went looking for Jesus.

Joe wasn't very hopeful. Everyone else drove him away, so why shouldn't Jesus just do the same? But he thought it was worth a try.

What a surprise he had! Jesus didn't drive him away. When he saw Joe coming, he stopped what he was doing and went to meet him. Well! That was rather different for a start! 'Hello,' he said, 'is there something I can do for you?' Joe was amazed! 'Aren't you afraid of me?' he asked, 'Don't you want to call me names and send me away?' 'Now why on earth would I want to do that?' asked Jesus. 'Everyone else does,' replied Joe, 'and you must admit I look pretty horrible!' 'But that's only on the outside,' said Jesus. Then he did the most wonderful thing. He walked right up to Joe, looked him in the eyes, reached out and took hold of his hand! 'Wow!' thought Joe, 'no-one's ever done that before – not since I got my skin disease.'

He was so surprised and excited that at first he didn't realise that Jesus had started speaking to him again. 'Now that I've touched you,' said Jesus, 'other people will, too. They won't be afraid of you any more. Go into the town, and people will be nice to you.'

It was then that Joe realised that his skin disease had gone. His skin was as smooth and healthy as it had been when he was a child! Joe was very, very happy. He went back to the farm and showed his parents. They were overjoyed and threw their arms around him. Now he could live at home again and have what he really most wanted – love and company.

Life was good again for Joe. He met up with his old friends again, children stopped being nasty to him, and he even got a job. But most of all, he felt loved and wanted. And all because of a man called Jesus, who reached out and touched him when nobody else would.

Based on Matthew 8:1-4

Let's Chat

What has happened today – to each of you? Have you met
anyone new, or anyone special?

We're Glad

Thank you God for lots of things,
especially happiness.
Thank you for fun
and the funny things
that have happened today (especially . . .)
Thank you for laughter.
Thank you for loving us.

We're Sad

God, sometimes bad things happen:
sometimes we get hurt,
sometimes we hurt other people.
often we hurt you.
Thank you for loving us,
even then.
Amen.

Let's Pray For People

Thank you God
for people we love,
and who love us,
especially . . .
look after (*her/him*)
Thank you for all our friends and our family,
and help us to love one another more.
Amen.

THE MAN WHO CAME IN THROUGH THE ROOF

B arney was a very wise and clever man who lived in a town called Capernaum, with his wife, Sarah. Everyone came to Barney if they had a problem and he would listen very carefully and ask a lot of questions. Very often, he didn't need to give any advice, because he asked such good questions that people began to think of the answers for themselves. You probably have teachers at school who do that kind of thing. But if he did decide to give someone advice, it was always good. People liked Barney because he cared and understood.

Then Barney became ill. He found that he couldn't use his arms and legs any more. He had to spend all day lying on his bed. The silly thing was that, although his brain was still perfectly alright, just because he couldn't walk people thought he couldn't do anything at all. So they all stopped coming to him for help. When friends visited Barney, they used to talk to Sarah about him, instead of talking to him. 'How is he, today?' they would ask – just as if he wasn't there! If they made him a drink, they would turn to Sarah and say, 'Does he take sugar?' They seemed to think that just because his legs wouldn't work, neither would his brain. What silly people!

Sarah got very unhappy about this, because she could see how much it hurt Barney. 'There must be something dreadfully wrong with me,' he used to say, 'for people to treat me this way. I wonder what I've done!' But most of all, Barney was worried about Sarah. 'I must be an awful problem to you,' he would say. This used to upset Sarah because, although looking after Barney wasn't easy, she loved him and did it willingly.

Then one day, Barney heard that Jesus was in town. 'Now there's someone who could help!' he thought. 'Sarah,' he called, 'see if you can find out where Jesus is.' Sarah did better than that. She came back with four of Barney's friends: Paul, Nick, Joe and Ben. 'We've found out where Jesus is,' said Ben, 'and we're going to take you to see him.' With that, they picked up his mattress, with him still on it, and carried him out of the door! 'Hey, hang on a minute!' cried Barney, 'I'm not ready. I've got to put some good clothes on and have a shave.' 'Don't be silly,' said Nick, 'd'you think Jesus cares what you look like?' It was no good Barney protesting any more, because by now they were half-way down the street.

Through the town they hurried, down alleyways and along main streets. Barney was getting more and more angry with the people they passed, who were looking at him and smiling in that silly way that adults often do towards babies! 'I'm a grown man!' he thought, 'Why do they treat me like a child!' Anyway, eventually they arrived at a house with a huge crowd gathered outside. 'This is the place,' said Paul, 'but how we're going to get in, I don't know.' 'Well, we haven't come all this way just to turn round and go home again,' said Joe, 'we've got to find a way.' 'I know,' said Ben, 'if we go up the stairs on to the roof, we can remove some tiles and lower him through the hole.' 'I suppose it might work,' said Nick, 'Paul, go and get some rope – there's a shop just back there.'

Inside the house, the people were all listening very hard to what Jesus was saying when, all of a sudden, they noticed noises coming from overhead. 'I think the roof's coming in,' shouted one frightened person, 'we'd better get out!' But just at that moment, the tiles were pulled off and Nick's bearded face appeared.

'I'm terribly sorry about this,' he said, 'But we've got someone here who's just got to see Jesus.' Then, to everybody's amazement, a mattress appeared and started to come down into the room. Jesus got up and went over, to see Barney lying on the mattress, looking very embarrassed!

'I'm sorry about this,' he said to Jesus, 'I'm afraid we have damaged your friend's roof.'

'Well,' said Jesus, 'I think my friend will get it fixed quite easily.'

'I really am sorry about the way I look,' said Barney, 'but my friends were so eager I didn't even get time to change my clothes, or have a shave.'

'You've no need to feel guilty,' said Jesus, 'feel good about yourself – God loves you!'

Some of the people around were surprised. 'He's got no right to say that kind of thing,' some of them said, 'only God can tell us not to feel guilty!' Jesus got very impatient at that. 'What silly people you are!' he exclaimed. 'No wonder this man's friends were so desperate!' Then he turned to Barney, and said, 'Why don't you get off that thing, roll it up and carry it back home with you?' With that, he took Barney's hand and lifted him to his feet. Barney was amazed to find strength in his legs once more. His four friends were excited, and Sarah was overjoyed! Barney thanked Jesus, and his friends, and hugged and kissed Sarah. Then he went home. On the way, he met people who were very surprised indeed to see him walking – so surprised that they actually talked to him, instead of to Sarah! By the time he got home, he'd made four appointments with people who wanted advice! Life was beginning again for Barney and Sarah!

Based on Mark 2:1-12

Let's Chat

What kind of things do you enjoy doing? Do you use lots of
energy? Can you do some things on your own,
or do you always need help?

We're Glad

Thank you, God, for our strength,
for all the things we can do, without needing help,
and for all the ways in which we can help one another.
(Most of all we enjoy . . .)
Thank you, God, very much.

We're Sad

Some people need help to do some things which may seem
'simple' to us, and so we behave as though they can't do
anything at all! They find that very annoying, because they
may be very good at other things, which we find difficult!

Dear God, sometimes we hurt people, without meaning to,
by trying too hard to be kind.
Sometimes we act as though people are stupid,
just because they can't walk, or can't hear.
Help us to remember that we all have something
we can't do.
Help us to be polite, and thoughtful
to those we call 'disabled'.

Let's Pray For People

Loving God, there are all kinds of people,
sharing the same world.
Some are very strong, some are very brainy,
some are very good at making things,
some paint, or draw, or write, or sing,
Everyone's good at something.
Help us *all* to be good
at being kind!

RAIN, RAIN, GO AWAY

J esus decided it was time to go home. It had been a long, hard day, and he was tired. He knew his friends were tired, too. The trouble was, they had to get across to the other side of Lake Galilee. So they had quite a journey ahead of them. 'Come on,' he said to his disciples, 'let's go home.'

So they got into the boat and pushed off into the lake. Peter was a little uneasy. He knew that storms could suddenly start on that lake, and their boat was not very big. So he told the rest of the disciples to keep a good look-out.

'You go up to the front Andrew,' said Peter, 'and Thomas, you go to the back. Keep a special watch on those clouds just over the hills – I don't like the look of them!' (I expect Peter would actually have said 'bow' and 'stern' normally, but not all the disciples were used to being in boats, so he made it easy for them.)

'Well,' said Jesus, 'I think I'll just go and lie down in the back of the boat.' And it wasn't long before he was fast asleep.

'What do those clouds look like, Thomas?' asked Peter. 'Not very good,' replied Thomas, 'they're very black, and they're coming this way.'

'Right!' said Peter, 'Philip, you and James get that sail down, or the wind will turn us right over. Judas and John, make sure all the heavy boxes are tied down, and everyone else, sit down and hang on tight!' He'd hardly got the words out before a sudden wind hit the boat and blew it out towards the middle of the lake. It whipped up the waves until they were as high as houses and the little boat was being tossed around on the top of the sea. Some of the waves came over the side, and the boat began to fill with water. Everyone was very frightened indeed. Everyone except Jesus that is, who was still fast asleep in the back. 'Well! Look at that!' said Thomas. 'We're working like mad to keep the boat afloat, and he's just lying there, sleeping!'

Peter went over to Jesus and shook him. 'Look,' he said, 'the boat's likely to sink any minute, and you're just lying there. Don't you care if we die?'

Jesus got up and went to the front of the boat. There he shouted to the wind and the sea. 'Stop it!' he said, 'Be quiet!' Peter was about to say, 'Well, a fat lot of good that will do!' when he noticed that it had gone quiet. The boat had stopped rocking and it wasn't filling with water any more. He tried to speak, but was so amazed that he just stood there, with his mouth open, looking for all the world like a fish! Jesus went over to him and put his hand on his shoulder. 'Why are you all so afraid?' he asked. 'Didn't you trust me?'

'Wh-wh-what's going on?' stammered Peter.

'Who is this man?' asked Andrew.

'I can't believe it!' said John, 'Even the wind and the sea do as he tells them!'

Jesus smiled and quietly went to sit in the back of the boat again, until they all got to the shore. 'There!' he said, 'Now we can all get some sleep!'

Based on Mark 4:35-41

Let's Chat

What kind of day has it been – cold, or warm, wet or dry?
What have you done? Have you enjoyed it?

We're Glad

God, our friend,
you give us all kinds of weather,
and all of it's good for someone.
Thank you for all of it:
for rain, for sun, for snow, for clouds.
And thank you for our home,
and our food.

We're Sad

Loving God, we're sorry
that we can't always be good.
We try very hard, but it isn't easy.
If we've hurt other people,
help us to make it right tomorrow.

Let's Pray For People

Dear God,
some people don't like it hot,
others complain when it's cold.
Some people like the sun,
others are happy when it's raining.
Some people are ill, or tired,
and get upset easily.
Help them to be happy,
and let them know you love them
whatever the weather's like.

GET UP, LITTLE GIRL

*J*airus was a very important man in the synagogue. Now some important people get very unpopular, because they act as though no-one else matters. But Jairus was not like that. He was always kind to the people who worked under him and if anyone was ill or unhappy Jairus would try and help. The word got around that Jairus was a very good man, and he had lots of friends in the town.

Jairus was married to Susie and they had a daughter called Hannah. Hannah was just like other girls – she loved to be outside playing in the sunshine with her friends, or exploring the caves in the hills just outside the town. If there was a tree in sight Hannah would climb it, and if there wasn't, well, she'd find something else. She was a very energetic little girl. She was also very caring about other people – rather like her parents. She would never hurt anyone by getting impatient with them (even though you and I might have thought they deserved it) and was most upset if she knew anyone was unhappy. Just like her father and mother, Hannah had lots of friends.

One day, when Hannah was about twelve years old, Susie noticed that Hannah didn't seem very well. She was sitting indoors, on a beautiful sunny day, and when her friends came to ask her out, she said, 'Not today, thank you; I think I'll just have a quiet day at home.' Susie was very worried. 'A quiet day at home?' she asked. 'You've never had a quiet day at home in all your life! Are you not feeling very well?' 'I'm all right,' said Hannah, 'I'd just like to stay in today, that's all.' Susie was really anxious. As the day went on, she noticed how pale Hannah was. 'Are you sure you're all right?' she asked. 'Of course I'm all right!' Hannah snapped at her, 'I keep *telling* you I'm all right, but still you keep on asking. Why can't you leave me alone?' And Hannah stamped off to her room, leaving Susie standing in the kitchen, with her mouth open in amazement.

When Jairus came in from work, Susie said, 'I'm terribly worried about Hannah. She's been really pale and quiet all day and this afternoon she actually shouted at me.' 'You're joking!' said Jairus, 'Hannah never shouts at anybody.' 'I assure you, I'm *not* joking,' replied Susie, who was nearly crying by now, 'Hannah shouted at me, stamped her foot and went to her room, and she hasn't come out since.' 'Well,' said Jairus, 'she must really be poorly. I'll go and have a look at her.' So he knocked on the door of Hannah's room and went in. As soon as he saw Hannah, he knew she was ill. 'You'd better go for the doctor,' he called out, and Susie hurried out to the surgery.

When Susie came back, she found Jairus looking really anxious. 'She won't speak to me,' he said, 'I don't know what to do.' The doctor hurried in. After a few moments, he came out to speak to Jairus and Susie. 'I'm afraid Hannah's got a very bad illness,' he explained, 'and there's nothing I can do to help.' Jairus and Susie were dreadfully upset. 'Do you mean she's not going to get better?' they asked. 'I'm sorry,' said the doctor, 'but I'm afraid it would take a miracle, and I don't do those.'

After the doctor had left, Jairus and Susie went to sit beside Hannah's bed and racked their brains trying to think of anyone else who could help them. The doctor's words, 'It would take a miracle', kept coming back into Susie's mind. 'Of course!' she said, 'I should have thought of it before! We know someone who can work miracles.' 'Yes,' said Jairus, 'Jesus works miracles. I don't know if he'd come though; some people at the synagogue have been saying unkind things about him.' 'Only because they're jealous,' replied Susie, 'and Jesus is too good a person to say no just because of that.' 'You're right,' said Jairus, 'I'll go and look for him.'

Jairus hunted everywhere – all the streets and little alleyways – until eventually he found Jesus. 'Please help me,' he gasped, 'my daughter's very ill, and only you can save her.' Jesus smiled at him. 'You'd better take me there,' he said, 'and don't worry – she'll be all right.' He had hardly got the words out when one of Jairus's neighbours came up. 'I'm terribly sorry, Jairus,' she said, 'but it's too late. Don't bother Jesus with it now – I'll take you home.' 'What do you mean, "Too late"?' asked Jesus. 'With God, it's *never* too late!

Don't worry Jairus, I said she'd be all right, and I don't break my promises.'

When they got to the house, it was full of neighbours and friends crying because Hannah was dead. 'Would you mind leaving, please,' said Jesus, 'so that I can get on?' 'I don't know what he thinks he can do,' mumbled one of them, 'I know a dead person when I see one.' But they went, leaving Jesus, Susie and Jairus with Hannah. Jesus went over to Hannah's bed and took her hand. 'Get up, little girl,' he said. And to the great amazement and joy of Susie and Jairus, Hannah's eyes opened.

'Hello,' she smiled, 'who are you?' 'My name's Jesus,' answered Jesus, 'what's yours?' 'Hannah,' she replied, 'and it's nice to meet you.' By this time, Jairus and Susie couldn't wait any longer. They rushed over to hug Hannah, who liked that very much, but wasn't really sure what was going on. 'Are you really all right?' asked Susie. 'Yes, Mother, of course I am,' answered Hannah, but in a very kind way, 'what on earth's the matter?' Then Susie and Jairus remembered Jesus. 'We can't thank you enough!' Susie said, 'Hannah was dead and now you've brought her back to us.' 'It was my pleasure,' said Jesus, 'but you'd better give her something to eat – she must be starving!'

Hannah looked very surprised. 'Eat?' she said, 'No time for that! It's a beautiful day – can't I go out to play?'

Based on Mark 5:22-43

Let's Chat

Jesus understood Hannah – because he loves
to enjoy life, as well!

We're Glad

Thank you, Jesus,
for wanting us to be happy.
It's good to be alive,
especially when people love us,
and care about us.
Help us to love life even more!

We're Sad

Forgive us please, Jesus,
for the times we've hurt people.
Sometimes, we've spoiled things,
made life hard for them,
because we've been selfish.
Whenever someone needs you,
you want to help them.
Help us to do the same.

Let's Pray for People

Let's pray for people who don't enjoy life.
Some people are lonely,
or perhaps they're ill.
Maybe they knew someone who has died.
Even when they're sad,
help them to know that life's worth living,
and help us to show them
that you care.

WHAT A CATCH!

S imon and his brother Andrew were having an argument. They were both fishermen and they had been out in their boat all night on Lake Galilee, but had not caught anything. 'It's your fault, Simon,' claimed Andrew, 'you took us to the wrong part of the lake.' 'Rubbish!' shouted Simon, angrily, 'You didn't bait the nets properly – you can't catch fish if the nets aren't baited properly.' 'You're the one who can't catch fish,' said Andrew, 'I've always done well when you haven't been with me.' Simon was getting angry. He was really a very kind man, but he had a quick temper, and he sometimes said and did things without thinking first. He was about to say to Andrew that in that case they'd better stop working together – and if he had said that then he would have been sorry later – when Andrew noticed something strange.

'Look, Simon,' he said, 'there's quite a crowd gathering just over there.' 'So there is! said Simon, 'Who's that guy talking to them? Isn't it Jesus, the carpenter?' 'That's right,' said Andrew, 'he's mended the boat for us a few times. I wonder what he's doing here.'

What Jesus was doing was teaching the crowd. Actually, he had stopped working as a carpenter, and was going around the towns and the countryside, telling people about God. When Simon and Andrew saw him, he was just beginning to get a bit worried, because the crowd were pushing to get close to him and, without meaning to, pushing *him* into the water! 'Hey, Jesus!' shouted Simon, 'You'd better get into our boat unless you want your feet washed!'

Jesus was very pleased with the invitation and got into the boat, which the brothers pushed out a little way from the bank. Then Jesus was able to stand and speak to the crowd, without being pushed into the lake. While he was talking, Andrew and Simon carried on tidying up the boat and quite forgot about their argument – especially when they started to listen to what Jesus was saying to the people. 'He's a good speaker, isn't he?' Simon whispered. 'Yes,' said Andrew, 'and what he's saying makes sense, too!'

When he had finished, Jesus said to Simon, 'Simon, why not go out a little bit further, now we're in the boat, and see if you can catch anything?'

'Oh, Jesus, do we have to?' asked Simon, 'We've been up fishing all of last night and haven't caught anything. I was looking forward to a quiet day.' 'The way you fish,' said Andrew, 'you'll get a lot of quiet days – and nights, as well.' 'Don't start all that again, Andrew,' said Jesus, 'I heard you before, when I was trying to teach. Come on Simon, put the boat out, and see what you can catch.' 'Well,' said Simon, 'as I said, we fished all last night and didn't get anything but, if you say so, I'll have another go.' 'I do say so, Simon,' said Jesus. So they got the boat moving. Andrew hoisted the sail, Simon untied the rope from the shore and before very long they were sailing out into the deep water where the fish usually were. It was a beautiful sunny day, with just enough breeze to move the fishing boat along.

When they got a few hundred metres out, Simon said, 'Where do you think we should try, Jesus?' 'Oh, I think just a bit further on yet,' Jesus answered. 'After all, it's a lovely day, so why hurry?' They carried on sailing for a few minutes and then Jesus said, 'I should think here would be about right, Simon.' All this time, Simon was secretly thinking, 'I don't know why I'm doing this! After all, he's a carpenter and I don't tell him how to make chairs! So why should he tell me where to fish?' But he didn't say it, partly because he liked Jesus and didn't want to hurt him, and partly because Jesus had a strange way of being right, and if Jesus said there were fish there, then there probably were, although how he knew was a mystery! So Simon and Andrew picked up the net between them and threw it over the side of the boat. They'd hardly done that when the boat lurched over to that side. 'We've snagged the net on something,' Simon called to Andrew.' 'We can't have done,' Andrew shouted back, 'the water's too deep.' 'Well then, we must have caught a whale!' Simon replied. Then they all realised. What they had caught was the biggest catch of fish they'd ever seen! The net was brimming over. All different kinds of fish were there and Simon decided they'd better get the net in before it broke.

'We'll never get it in,' said Andrew, huffing and puffing as he pulled at the net, 'and if we do, it'll probably break.' 'Well, we can't leave it there,' said Simon, 'or it'll pull the boat over!' Then Andrew noticed James and John, sailing nearby in their boat. 'They'll help us,' he said, and he raised his voice. 'Hey, James, over here – give us a hand!' James and John realised that the other boat was in trouble and came over to help. They held the net between the two boats and got it to the shore. 'How did you get all those fish?' John asked, 'We'd just been over there and got nothing!' 'I don't know,' said Simon, 'I just did what Jesus told me.'

Based on Luke 5:1-11

Let's Chat

Has everything gone well today, or have some things
gone wrong? What has been most enjoyable,
and what has been worst about today?

We're Glad

Thank you, Jesus, for everything good
that has happened today,
especially when we didn't expect it!
Thank you for helping us to get things right,
and thank you for giving us people who help us, as well.
Thank you, Jesus.

We're Sad

Not everything has gone well today, Jesus,
some people have been disappointed.
Perhaps we could have been more helpful
to each other, or to other people.
We're sorry if we've let anyone down. Please forgive us.

Let's Pray For People

Some people, like doctors, or train drivers, or airline pilots,
dare not risk making mistakes. Even then, they still get things
wrong and sometimes the results are dreadful.
Let's pray for people in very important jobs,
who dare not make mistakes:
people like doctors, and train drivers, (and . . .)
Please, Jesus, be helpful to people
who have important jobs.
Help them not to make mistakes, and if they do,
forgive them, and help them to forgive themselves.

THE SOLDIER WHO BELIEVED IN JESUS

M arcus was an officer in the Roman army. He was called a Centurion, which means that he was in charge of a hundred other men. That meant he was quite an important person. He had a servant called Septimus who took messages, made sure he always had a clean uniform and generally looked after him, leaving him to spend his time being a good soldier. Marcus was quite an unusual Roman soldier. Normally, they were hard and cruel people and the people of Israel hated them, but not many people hated Marcus. 'You know,' said Septimus one day, as he was hanging up Marcus's tunic, 'since you built them that synagogue, to worship God in, they love you even more than before.' 'I didn't do it for that reason,' said Marcus, 'I just don't see why we have to be cruel to people, just because we've beaten them in war. Mostly, they're good, honest people and I like them.' 'But they never come to visit us, do they?' said Septimus. 'They can't,' Marcus replied, 'because they have a law against it. A lot of them think it's as silly as we do, but they have to obey it all the same.'

It was true that they didn't get visitors. No matter how good someone might be, if they were of a different religion they were never fully accepted by the other people, at that time.

One day, Septimus fell ill. The army doctor was called in, but he couldn't help. 'I'm sorry,' he said to Marcus, 'but I'm afraid he's going to die.' Marcus was very upset. He had come to think of Septimus more as a friend than as a servant and he didn't want him to die. But he didn't see what he could do. So he went to the market to buy Septimus some nice, juicy grapes. 'At least I can try to cheer him up a bit,' he thought. When he was out in the market-place, people kept asking him where Septimus was, because they were normally seen together. 'I'm afraid he's very ill,' said Marcus, sadly, 'and the army doctor says he can't make him better.' Everyone was very upset about that and then a fig-merchant called Jud spoke up. 'I know who could help him,' he said, 'there's a man called Jesus around these parts who heals people every day. Let's go and get Jesus – he was in the main square, last thing I heard.' With that, some of the traders ran off to look for Jesus, leaving their stalls with nobody to look after them.

'It's no good asking him to come here,' said Marcus, 'he won't be able to go into the house.' 'Too late,' said Nathan, a carpet-seller, 'they've already gone to get him.' 'But from what I've heard, he doesn't need to come, anyway.' said Marcus, 'He's so powerful that all he has to do is say the word – even from a long way away. Nathan, could you go after them, and take this message?' 'What am I, your messenger-boy?' replied Nathan, but he went anyway, because he liked Marcus and Septimus as much as the others did. So Marcus wrote a note and Nathan ran off with it.

It wasn't long before Jud and his friends found Jesus. He was talking with some of his special friends, under the shade of a large palm tree. 'Sir! Sir!' shouted Jud, 'You've got to come quickly – someone's dying.' 'Who's dying?' asked Jesus. 'Septimus is,' said Jud. 'He's the servant of a Roman centurion called Marcus.' One of the people nearby turned and said, 'Septimus, dying? That's terrible. Marcus might be a soldier, but he's been really good to us.' 'Yes,' added someone else, 'he even paid for our synagogue to be built.'

Jesus set off straight away to find Marcus, with Jud and his friends leading the way. Before they had got very far, Nathan came running up, panting for breath. 'Thank goodness I've found you!' he spluttered, 'I'm too old for this kind of thing.' 'Just a minute,' said Jesus, 'Get your breath back, and then tell me what you want.' 'Just read this,' said Nathan. Jesus took the note from him, and this is what it said:

Dear Jesus,

Please don't come to my house. I'm a soldier, and not of your religion. I know all about obeying orders and, because I'm an officer, I know what giving orders is about. I tell people to 'Come here,' and they do. I say, 'Go there,' and they do. So I know that if you just say the word, Septimus will be well again.

Yours sincerely,
Marcus

Jesus read the note aloud, and then turned to his special friends. 'Did you hear that?' he asked them, 'This man is not of our religion, he doesn't worship with us and he doesn't say the same kind of prayers as we do. But he's got a lot more faith than most people of our own religion have. I've never heard anything like it before – not even in Israel!'

Then Jesus turned to Nathan. 'Go back to Marcus,' he said, 'and tell him that Septimus is better.' Nathan couldn't wait! He went off like a rocket, with Jud and the others just behind. When they got to the market again, Marcus was just leaving to go home. 'I've had a message from home,' he said, smiling happily, 'Septimus is well! What do you think of that?' 'Wonderful!' said Nathan, and he meant it as well, but there was just a little thing that was worrying him. 'D'you know what else the healer said?' he asked Marcus. 'No,' said Marcus, 'tell me.' 'Well,' said Nathan, thoughtfully, 'he said that you had more faith than any of us. And you don't even believe in our religion.'

'Well!' said Marcus, 'What a strange thing to say!' But he didn't stop to think about it. He was too eager to get home and see Septimus again.

Based on Luke 7:1-11

Let's Chat

Do people sometimes surprise you by doing things you don't expect? For example, do 'unkind' people sometimes do kind things, or 'dull' people sometimes have brilliant ideas?

We're Glad

Lord Jesus,
you know what people are like.
You know that sometimes we surprise each other.
Thank you for nice surprises,
thank you for making life so exciting!

We're Sad

We're sorry, Jesus,
for the times when we're unfair to people.
Just because they're different from us,
we think that they can't do things,
or that we shouldn't trust them.
Sometimes that makes them sad.
Help us not to be prejudiced.

Let's Pray For People

Loving God,
we pray for people who are different,
and who get left out.
Help us to realise that, to some other people,
we are the ones who are different.
We wouldn't like to be left out because of that.
Help us to be kind.
And help us to see that wonderful people
come in all shapes, sizes and colours!

A VERY UNHAPPY PERSON

A t one time, Anna was a very happy person. She had a husband, Abe, who loved her very much, and two sons, John and David, who thought that she was the best mum in the world. Abe had a good job at the local quarry and they were doing good trade at the time, because the army barracks was being extended and the governor wanted lots of stone for the buildings. That meant that Abe had plenty of work and when John and David grew up they would probably get good jobs, too. Everything looked good, until Anna got ill. 'Go and see the doctor,' said Abe, 'we can afford to pay.' In those days, you had to pay the doctor every time you went, but Anna wasn't worried: 'It won't be anything serious,' she thought, 'and we shall be able to afford the treatment.'

The doctor gave her an examination and said, 'Hmm . . . I'm not too sure about this. I think I'll send you to see a specialist.' 'I don't mind that,' said Anna, 'how much will it be?' 'Well,' said the doctor, 'that depends. The local one has a long waiting list and you will need to take your turn. But I know someone in Jerusalem who's very good and he could see you more quickly. The only trouble is, he costs more and, of course, there's the camel fare.' 'I'll go to him,' said Anna. And she did. But he couldn't help her either and sent her to somebody else. Well, this went on for a long time and no-one seemed able to cure Anna. Eventually, Abe said, 'I'm sorry, but we can't afford any more of these expensive doctors.' 'I'll just have to accept it,' said Anna, 'no-one can cure me.' Then she began to think, 'It must be me – I must be a bad person and God doesn't want me to get better.' So she decided just to put up with it. She and Abe became very unhappy, but they tried not to let John and David see it.

Then she heard about a man called Jesus, who could heal people even when the doctors couldn't. And, best of all, he didn't charge for it! When she heard he was in town, she could hardly believe her luck! She put on her best clothes and went out to meet him. But when she saw him, she became very nervous.

'What if I was right?' she wondered, 'What if I'm a bad person, being punished? He's obviously a holy man – I'd better not trouble him.' So she began to go away. Then an idea came to her. 'If he's so wonderful, perhaps I don't need to ask him. Perhaps I could just touch his coat,' she thought. So she crept up behind him, and touched just the edge it.

It worked! She was better already! The pain began to get less and she felt full of energy, as though she could jump over the moon! But then a really frightening thing happened. Jesus stopped. He turned round and asked, 'Who touched me?' Peter, one of his friends, laughed. 'Look,' he said, 'there are people all around you, all pushing and shoving and you ask who touched you!' 'Yes, I did,' said Jesus, 'and I want to know.'

He obviously wasn't going to take 'no' for an answer. So Anna plucked up all her courage and went to him. 'I touched you,' she said, 'I'm really sorry if you're cross, but I've been ill all this time and none can help me and I thought that if I . . .' Then she stopped, because she had noticed that the look in Jesus' eyes was of real gentleness and love. 'Don't apologise,' he said, 'the question is, do you feel better?' 'Oh, yes!' she exclaimed, 'Heaps and heaps better!' 'Good,' said Jesus, 'that's because you had faith. But you should never have been afraid to come to me. It doesn't matter how bad you think you are, you can always face me.' Anna was over the moon! Touching Jesus' coat had cured her illness but something much better had happened. Because she'd actually met him, he'd even been able to make her feel good about herself. 'I can't be a bad person,' she thought, and she went dashing home to Abe, to tell him about it. Abe saw her running up the garden path and nearly died from shock! 'How long have you been able to do that?' he asked. 'Oh, about ten minutes!' laughed Anna, and gave him an enormous hug. That evening they had a special dinner to celebrate what had happened. Life was good once more. Anna could enjoy being with Abe and the boys, without the worry her illness had caused; she never thought bad things about herself again, and she always remembered a man called Jesus who had changed her life.

Based on Luke 8:43-48

Let's Chat

Think about people you love, and who love you. Doesn't it
feel good, knowing people love you!

We're Glad

Jesus, it feels good,
knowing people love us,
and especially
knowing you love us.
Thank you for loving us,
and thank you for showing it
by giving us each other.

We're Sad

Jesus you loved people,
even when others didn't.
Sometimes we find it hard
to love people.
Sometimes we hurt them,
make them feel guilty.
We're sorry.

Let's Pray For People

Jesus, some people feel bad
because they're ill,
or because they feel ashamed.
Some people think no one loves them
and that they must be bad.
Jesus, be a friend to them
and help us to be friends to them, too.
Amen.

'SUNDAY TRADING'

R achel was not at all happy. She had been ill for eighteen years! It was a strange illness that made it impossible for her to stand up. She had been to lots of doctors, but none of them could help. They'd tried all kinds of things, but nothing worked. Now, she had almost no money left and it looked as though she was going to be bent double for the rest of her life. It was a great shame, because she used to be very fit at one time, going for long walks, swimming in the rivers and lakes and even taking part in the town's annual 'Donkey Derby'! Now, she had had to stop doing all those things and rely on other people to help her. Even simple things like hanging out the washing were impossible, because she couldn't reach the line. The worst thing was that she wasn't particularly old, but life seemed to have lost all its meaning for her. She longed to be able to walk upright like other people and perhaps play some games with the children. She couldn't even look up and see the sky without a great effort.

One Saturday, she was in the synagogue at worship. In those days, Saturday was rather like our Sunday. It was called the 'Sabbath', which means it was set aside for people to rest. People went to the synagogue to worship God and no-one was allowed to do any work which was not really necessary. They were very strict about that – some people thought a little too strict. It was good to have a day of rest, of course, and it was good for almost everyone to rest on the same day, because it meant that life was quieter. So everybody was happy with that. The trouble was that the people who made the laws had made it so strict that it sometimes got silly. You couldn't even go and see your friends, if they lived any distance away, because walking counted as work, unless it was to the synagogue of course! This particular day, Jesus was teaching in the synagogue, and he saw Rachel come in, all bent double, and obviously in pain. So he went over to her, to see whether he could help.

'What's the matter?' Jesus asked, 'Can't you stand up straight?' 'I haven't stood up straight for eighteen years!'

replied Rachel, and then added, 'And even if I could I'd keep my head down in this place.' 'Why's that?' asked Jesus. 'Well,' said Rachel, 'we women don't have much of a place in the synagogues do we? Even if I could stand up straight, I'd probably be frightened to, in case someone noticed me!' 'That's silly,' said Jesus, 'everyone should be able to hold their head up proudly in God's house.' And as he said it, he took her by the hand and lifted her up. And do you know what happened? Her back straightened, her head came up, and she looked right into Jesus' eyes! Everyone was amazed and a lot of them were very pleased. But there was at least one person who wasn't. Jerry, the leader of the synagogue was angry. He *said* he was cross with Jesus for 'working' on the Sabbath day, but some people thought it was other things he was really worried about. Some people, like him, just didn't like Jesus very much and were always trying to catch him out. 'You've broken the law,' he said to Jesus, 'you've worked on the day of rest.' 'You can't call that work,' said Jesus, 'all I did was take her hand and help her to stand up straight. Don't you want her to be able to stand up straight in God's house?' 'That's not the point,' said Jerry, 'we all know you're a healer – so healing is work and you shouldn't do it on a rest day. You've got the other six days for doing that.' Jesus thought this was really very silly indeed, and very cruel. 'What if she was a farm animal who had fallen into a well?' he asked, 'Would it be alright for me to go and pull her out?' 'That's different,' shouted Jerry, getting very angry. 'the law says you can do that, because it's an emergency.' 'So,' said Jesus, 'the law thinks that a farm animal is more important than a woman!' Everyone laughed at that – except for Jerry, who just got more and more angry, because people like that don't like being laughed at, at all!

Jesus went on, and said, 'You can rescue animals on the rest day, and you can feed them, so of course, a woman who's had to put up with illness for eighteen years should be freed from it on the same day! She's just as important as you or anyone else, and don't you ever forget it.' Jerry could not find any answer to that and he was very embarrassed. The rest of the people were really overjoyed. 'That was the best service we've been to for a long time,' many of them said – and that just made Jerry jump up and down all the more!

As for Rachel, she went home, singing and dancing as she went, looking up at the beautiful blue sky and stopping to play with every child she met on the way. From now on, life was going to be very different indeed!

Based on Luke 13:10-17

Let's Chat

Do you have 'rules'? Are there things you aren't allowed
to do? What about rules that adults have to obey?
Why do you think we have them?

We're Glad

Loving God,
thank you for caring for us,
and for showing us
the best way to live.
Thank you for telling us
to care for one another
and giving us rules
to keep us safe.

We're Sad

We're sorry, Jesus,
for our selfishness.
We're sorry if anybody has been hurt,
because we've been too fussy.
Forgive us and help us to remember
that the most important rule
is to love each other.

Let's Pray For People

Jesus, our friend,
be a special friend to all those who are in prison.
Help them to know that you love them,
and that we are praying for them.
And help us to be kind to people we know
who get into trouble.

JESUS AND THE TAX MAN

*T*his is a story about Jesus meeting a man called Zacchaeus. Zacchaeus was rather a small man – the kind who can easily get lost in a crowd. He seemed to spend all his life looking upwards when he was talking to people. Of course some very cruel people, including some children, used to tease Zacchaeus dreadfully. They called him names like 'Titch' and 'Shorty'. Sometimes, when they thought they were being really funny, they'd call him 'Lofty' which was even worse!

Zacchaeus might not have minded the teasing so much if he'd thought that, underneath it all, people actually liked him. After all, people do tease other people whom they like – they may even call them the same names – but they do it differently. The way people spoke to Zacchaeus, he knew that they didn't like him one little bit. The trouble was that the people thought he was a cheat. He might have been, of course, but there again he might not. People aren't always right. Certainly, he was very rich, but that wouldn't have made people hate him. The real trouble was that he was a tax collector. It was his job to see that people paid their taxes, and nobody likes someone who does that! So a lot of people said that he charged people more than he should have done and kept the extra for himself. It might have been untrue, but nobody cared, because they liked having a go at Zacchaeus. They didn't realise just how unhappy that made him.

Anyway, one day Zacchaeus heard that Jesus was coming to the town where he lived. How he would love to see Jesus! He'd never met him, but he'd heard a lot about him. He'd heard that Jesus loved everybody. 'I wonder if he would even love me?' he thought, 'He'd be the first one, if he did!' So he had a wash, trimmed his beard and went out into the street to look out for Jesus.

But the trouble was that there were lots of crowds and, because Zacchaeus was small, he couldn't see. So he climbed a tree to get a better view. Of course, the crowd loved it when they saw where Zacchaeus was. You can imagine them shouting nasty things like, 'Look at Zacchaeus, up a tree – now that's where he ought to live!' But they were soon distracted when Jesus arrived, and forgot about Zacchaeus.

Jesus saw Zacchaeus, sitting in the tree, and called out to him,' Zacchaeus, what are you doing there?' 'Looking for you, actually!' said Zacchaeus. 'Well, you won't find me up there,' said Jesus, 'get down and go home – I'm coming to have dinner with you.' 'What me?' said Zacchaeus, 'Why do you want to come and see me?' 'Well, not to pay my taxes,' said Jesus, 'they're up to date! Look Zacchaeus, does there have to be a reason?' 'I suppose not,' replied Zacchaeus. 'Good,' said Jesus, 'because my feet ache, my eyes hurt from the sun and my stomach's shouting out for food. So come down here and let's go and eat.'

Now, most people thought that Jesus was a good man. So they couldn't understand why he was going to have dinner with Zacchaeus. Sharing food with someone usually meant that they were a special friend and everyone thought that being a good person was more important than anything else. They also thought that you could catch naughtiness, rather like a disease. For all those reasons, people who thought they were good didn't have meals with people they thought were bad! So some people were angry with Jesus. 'He shouldn't go in there,' they said, 'Zacchaeus is a bad man!'

Zacchaeus was just as amazed as everyone else! 'Who'd have thought,' he wondered, 'that Jesus would come to have dinner with me!' Then he thought that if Jesus could like him enough to do that, then others might as well. He wasn't really such a bad person, after all! So he stood up and made a speech.

'Here and now,' he said,'I'm giving half of everything I have to charity.' 'Wow!' thought all the people (who had followed to watch what happened, but had never expected this!), but that wasn't all.

'If I've cheated anyone,' Zacchaeus went on, 'they can come to see me, and I'll give them back four times as much!'

From then on, Zacchaeus became a kinder, happier man and everyone wanted to go and have dinner with him!

Based on Luke 19:1-10

Let's Chat

Are there people you don't like very much?
How well do you really know them?
Might they be nicer than you think?

We're Glad

Jesus, you know us.
You know what is good and what is bad in us.
and you love us just the same. Thank you.

We're Sad

Sometimes we love other people,
but sometimes we don't.
Sometimes, we're kind to people,
but sometimes we're not.
Sometimes, we say people are bad,
when we don't really know. We're sorry.
Help us to see that everybody
has something good about them.
And forgive us when we're unkind.

Let's Pray for People

Jesus, we know that some people are unhappy,
because others are unkind to them.
Teach us all to be like you,
and to love all people,
whether we think they deserve it,
or whether we think they don't.
Then, perhaps, we might find out
good things about them.
Jesus, make us like you. Amen.

THE DONKEY'S DAY OUT

W ell, there I was, standing in the shade, munching on a mouthful of hay – because that's what donkeys do – when along came these two men, whom I'd never seen before in my life and started to untie me from the wall. I suppose some donkeys would have been pleased to be untied, freedom and all that, but I knew there was a catch. Whenever someone unties me, it's because they've got work for me to do and, as it was a hot day and the hay was tasty, I wasn't very keen. Besides, my mother always told me not to go off with strangers. So I just dug my hooves into the ground and refused to budge! You should have seen those two men trying to move me! They both got hold of the rope and pulled, then one of them went round the back and pushed. I could have kicked him but that would have been unkind – besides, I was enjoying the fun! They weren't though, they got angrier every second. And they used some words which well-brought-up religious people shouldn't even have known about! Then, just as it was getting really interesting, my master came out and spoilt it. 'Hey!' he shouted, 'What do you think you're doing with my donkey?' And one of the men (who I later found out was called Thomas) said, 'The master needs it.' (What a cheek – fancy calling a respectable donkey 'it'!) I expected my master to say, 'Yes, and I'm the master – put him back!' but he didn't. Obviously it was someone else's master who needed me and to my amazement, my master just said, 'Oh, all right then,' and told me to stop mucking about. I nearly said, 'Mucking about? You ain't seen nothing yet!' but I decided not to. So off we went, and I'm glad because I had the time of my life!

When we got near to the town of Jerusalem, we met up with a group of people, led by a man they called Jesus. I felt something soft being put on my back and then someone sat on me. I couldn't see who it was, but I worked out that it was Jesus and obviously he was 'the master'. We set off into the town, and you should have heard the racket! Someone shouted, 'Look who's coming!' and before we knew it, the streets were full of people. They were singing, they were dancing and spreading their clothes on the road, making a carpet for me to walk on. Don't you do that sort of thing though, or you won't half get into trouble. Human parents are really fussy about clothes! I wanted to say thank you, but I remembered some more advice my mother gave me. 'Never talk to humans,' she'd said, 'it upsets them – they like to think they're the only ones who can do it.' So I kept my mouth shut and kept on going. It was wonderful. All these people must have realised what a special donkey I was and came running to meet me. Then I cottoned on: it was Jesus, not me, they were shouting for. They thought he was some sort of a king. Well if he was a king, I was the king's donkey, so I was still special, wasn't I?

As we got into the town, I was getting a bit worried. What about King Herod? He wasn't going to like people saying that Jesus was a king, was he? I hoped there wasn't going to be any trouble. Then some of the important leaders came over, looking very worried, and said to Jesus, 'Can't you shut this rabble up? It's going to cause no end of trouble.' But Jesus laughed, 'Shut them up? Impossible! There's so much joy around today that if the people didn't shout, the stones probably would!' That told them! They looked very grumpy when they went away, and I was glad because I'd met one of them before. He'd walked past when I was tied up outside the temple one day and tried to push me out of the way. I wasn't going to move without being asked, and he got cross and kicked me. He was lucky I didn't kick back. Anyway, I really enjoyed seeing Jesus get the better of him, that day.

I must admit I got a bit worried – I thought for a minute that Jesus was actually going to try to take over and revolutions aren't really my thing. But he didn't do anything of the sort. He went to the temple and caused a bit of a scene, but I didn't see much of that, because I was tied up outside. I just heard a lot of noise and saw some people running out with animals and birds all over the place. It turned out that the men were market traders. What had they been doing selling things in the temple in the first place is what I'd like to know.

I heard later that Jesus had said something like that, and driven them out. Anyway, when he came out, two more of his friends, Philip and Andrew, took me home. On the way, Philip said, 'It's strange, why didn't he find himself a horse to ride instead of this scruffy little donkey, then he'd have looked more like a king.' (I tell you, I nearly stopped and refused to go another step! 'Scruffy little donkey,' indeed! But my mum always said, 'Never cut off your nose to spite your face,' so, as we were going home and I was tired, I pretended I hadn't heard.) Andrew explained. 'Jesus doesn't want to be that kind of king – the kind everyone's afraid of. He wants to be a gentle king. He loves the people and he wants them to love him. So he didn't want anything impressive – just an ordinary mule.' It got worse! 'Ordinary'! and 'Mule'! I bet I've got a better pedigree than either of those two fellows had! They will never know how close they came to being in real trouble. But we were nearly home, so I just kept on going.

I liked Jesus – he seemed different. Most riders kick me with their heels to make me walk, but he didn't. It's nice to get a bit of respect. Yes, I like Jesus. But his friends – oh dear! I'm afraid they've got an awful lot to learn!

Based on Luke 19:29-40

Let's Chat

Do you know some bossy people,
who think they're terribly important? Aren't they awful!
You would never be like that, of course, would you?

We're Glad

Thank you Jesus,
for loving us,
and wanting us to love you.
Thank you for being kind to us,
and for not bossing us around!

We're Sad

We're not always kind to other people.
Sometimes we like to be bossy,
when we don't need to be;
we want people to think we are good,
and we end up by hurting them,
and making ourselves look silly
at the same time.
We're sorry.
Help us to love people more.

Let's Pray for People

We know that some people have to give orders,
and everyone has to take them from somebody.
We pray for people who tell others what to do:
help them to be kind,
to show respect,
to love, and to be loved.

A STRANGER ON THE ROAD

C leopas and Joanna were friends of Jesus. They were also friends of each other – in fact they were married! They were usually very happy. They had a home in a village called Emmaus, about seven miles from Jerusalem, and although it wasn't a palace they'd fixed it up very nicely, so that it was warm and welcoming, and they enjoyed being there together.

Our story begins, though, in Jerusalem. They had gone there over the weekend for a big festival and had expected to have a really good time. They had been particularly excited about seeing Jesus. 'I know he'll be there,' Joanna had said, 'because I was over in Bethany the other day, and Martha told me he was going to stay with them.' So they had gone to Jerusalem, to the festival, full of hope and really looking forward to seeing Jesus. But everything seemed to have gone wrong. When they got there, they heard that Jesus had been captured by some bad people, and had been killed. What they didn't know, on this particular Sunday evening, was that God had brought Jesus back to life, and he was at that very moment walking around Jerusalem, and planning to go to Emmaus to see them.

'Let's go home,' said Joanna, 'I don't like it here any more.' 'Neither do I,' said Cleopas, 'everyone seems frightened, and the place is full of terrible memories.' So they said goodbye to their friends and set out to walk the seven miles home. It was beginning to get dark, and they got a little nervous when a stranger began to catch up with them. Cleopas took a firm hold on the stick he was carrying, just in case. Meanwhile, Joanna was saying, 'I can't understand how it happened. Jesus had so many friends, you'd have thought they'd have stopped it.' 'Stopped what?' asked the stranger, who had drawn level with them. 'Well!' said Cleopas, who was relieved that the stranger seemed friendly, 'You've obviously been in Jerusalem, and you must be the only person not to know what's happened.' 'Why?' asked the stranger, 'What has happened.' 'You must have been walking around with your eyes closed!' said Cleopas, 'Jesus, the great teacher and healer, was killed – just because some powerful people were jealous of him.' 'Oh, that,' said the stranger, 'didn't you expect that to happen? If you'd been reading your bible, you might have done. People like Jesus always seem to get on the wrong side of powerful people.' 'We did hear a rumour that God had brought him back to life,' said Joanna. 'Yes I know,' said Cleopas impatiently, 'but that was just some silly women – we men knew it couldn't be true!'

What Cleopas and Joanna did not know was that this stranger was none other than Jesus himself! The 'silly women' had been right! It may seem strange that they didn't recognise him, but of course it was getting dark and he probably had a hood up because the road was very dusty. Anyway, they didn't recognise him. So he spent the journey walking with them and talking about the bible, and what it said. It was certainly true that the bible said that God's special helper was going to get himself into an awful lot of trouble! By the time they got home to Emmaus, they were beginning to feel a bit better. 'It's a dreadful shame that Jesus was killed,' said Cleopas, 'but perhaps God's at work in all this somewhere.' 'Oh, yes, I think he is,' said the stranger mysteriously, 'God doesn't like bad things happening, but sometimes he can do the most amazing things with them!'

By this time, they were at the door of Cleopas' and Joanna's house. 'Boy, am I glad to be home!' exclaimed Joanna, 'Here we can feel safe. Nothing exciting happens here and we always know where we stand.' 'Really?' said the stranger, 'I wouldn't bank on that, if I were you. Still, it's been nice meeting you. Goodnight.' And he started to move on.

'Just a minute,' called Cleopas after him, 'it's getting late. Wouldn't you like to come and stay with us?' 'Thank you very much,' said the stranger, and together they went into the house. It was certainly very welcoming. Joanna and Cleopas soon had a warm fire going and had put some bread on the table for a meal. Just as Cleopas was about to offer the food round, the stranger did a very odd thing. *He* picked up the bread, broke it into pieces and began to hand it round. 'That's strange,' thought Cleopas, 'he's our guest, and we're supposed to wait on him – but he's serving us.' Suddenly Joanna exclaimed, 'Good heavens! It's Jesus!' Then Cleopas remembered where he'd seen Jesus do that before and he looked carefully at the stranger. 'So it is!' he cried, joyfully, and he and Joanna both went to hug Jesus at the same time. But he wasn't there! He'd gone!

'Did we dream that?' asked Cleopas. 'Not unless we both had the same dream!' replied Joanna, 'anyway, look, there's his plate with the broken bread on it.' 'Come on!' said Cleopas, 'We've got to get back.' Well, you wouldn't have thought it was seven long miles to Jerusalem. They scurried back, puffing and panting, and burst into the room where the other friends of Jesus were staying. 'Guess what!' panted Joanna. 'No,' said Philip, '*you* guess what! Jesus is alive again – it's true. We know it's true, because Simon told us.' Joanna nearly said, 'Oh, so you believe a man, do you?' but she didn't want to spoil the evening. Everyone was wonderfully happy. They kept on telling the stories to each other of how they had found out. Mind you, none of the men apologised to the women for not believing them in the first place, but all the quarrels were forgotten, and they spent the rest of the night celebrating.

'Just think,' said Cleopas to Joanna, 'A few hours ago, Jerusalem was a terrible place to be. And now it's the best place on earth!' 'Yes,' said Joanna, 'that often seems to happen when Jesus is around – even when we don't recognise him!' Everyone laughed at that and Peter proposed the traditional Jewish toast. 'To life!' he said. 'To life!' everybody shouted.

Based on Luke 24:13-35

Let's Chat

Do you sometimes feel like running away?

We're Glad

Thank you, Jesus,
for being our friend.
Thank you for always being with us,
wherever we are,
and whatever we're doing.
Thank you for never leaving us
to cope on our own.

We're Sad

Sometimes, we run away,
just when people need us.
We don't want to face up to things,
or do difficult jobs.
We're sorry, Jesus,
help us to be brave.

Let's Pray for People

Please, God, help people who are frightened,
and who want to run away.
Help them to know that you're still there,
still caring.
And if they can't recognise you,
because they're confused or unhappy,
show us the best way to help them.

A WEDDING WITH NO WINE

J ake and Sarah were a lovely couple, who lived in a town called Cana, not far from Nazareth where Jesus lived. Jake was a tailor with a little workshop where he made and mended clothes for the local people, and he had been saving his money for a long time, because he and Sarah were getting married. They, and all their friends, were very excited about it. They'd made arrangements with the Rabbi; they'd been to see the caterers about the reception; Jake had made himself a new set of clothes, and Sarah's mother had bought her a beautiful dress. One day, they were discussing who they should invite as guests. 'Of course,' said Sarah, 'our parents will have to be there, and our neighbours. I'd like to invite Abie and Rachel, because they've been really good friends to us.' 'Yes,' said Jake, 'and it would be good to invite Jesus, the carpenter. After all, he's made us some lovely furniture.' 'We should invite his mother, as well,' said Sarah. 'Yes,' said Jake, 'Mary's a lovely person – she's got to be there.' And so the conversation went on, until they'd got the guest list sorted out, and they sent out the invitations. Everything was ready. When the big day came, all the neighbourhood turned out to see the couple pass by on their way to the wedding, and quite a lot of them actually went to the ceremony. Jake and Sarah promised to love each other for the rest of their lives, and everybody cheered. Then they went to the reception. Of course, the usual speeches were made. Everyone said what a lovely couple Sarah and Jake were and, every few minutes, someone would raise a glass and shout 'to life!' and everyone would shout back, 'to life!', and they'd drink a toast.

The caterer was getting worried. 'They're drinking a lot more than I expected,' he said, 'and I think the wine's going to run out before long.' He'd hardly got the words out when his head waiter came up, looking very worried, and said, 'We've run out of wine.' 'Oh dear!' said the caterer, 'Already? What on earth are we going to do?' 'I don't know,' said the head waiter, 'but you'd better think of something, or you'll never be asked to do another wedding within a hundred miles of here!'

Mary, Jesus' mother, had overheard the conversation and whispered to Jesus, 'I think they've run out of wine. Can you do anything to help?' At first, Jesus wasn't very keen. 'I didn't really come here for that purpose,' he said. But Mary knew that he wouldn't let people go thirsty, so she went over to the caterer and said, 'My son's over there – the tall one, second from the end of the third table – if you ask him, he'll be able to help.' So the caterer went over to Jesus, and said, 'Er, I'm afraid this is rather embarrassing, sir, but . . .' 'I bet it is,' smiled Jesus, 'you've run out of wine, haven't you? Well, you'll have to use those big jugs of water over there by the door.' In those days, because there were no proper roads, people got very dusty from walking, and whenever someone came to visit you would give them water to wash their feet, in the same way as we would take their coat and hang it up for them. It was good manners. And that was what the jars of water were for. The caterer was horrified. 'You can't use that!' he said, 'It's not even drinking water – it's straight from the river!' 'Don't argue with him,' said Mary, 'trust him, and do whatever he says.' 'Well,' said the caterer, gloomily, 'I suppose anything's worth a try when you're desperate.' And he sent two waiters to go and bring the jars to Jesus. The jars were very heavy! 'Now what do we do?' gasped one of the waiters. 'Pour some of it out,' said Jesus, 'and take it to Jake to taste it.' The waiter thought Jesus was potty, but his boss just nodded at him. So they poured out a glassful and took it to Jake. The waiter didn't hang around to see what happened, but went out to help with the washing up – anything was better than being around when Jake tasted the dirty water! Sure enough, he heard Jake shouting, 'Where's the caterer? Someone find me the caterer!' 'Oh dear,' thought the waiter, 'now we're for it, but he did tell me to do it, so he can't blame me.' The caterer went over to Jake, thinking he'd have to apologise, and blame the waiter for making a mistake, but he found Jake smiling and very, very pleased! 'You've saved the best wine until the end!' he exclaimed. 'Most caterers use the worst wine at the end, because they think the guests will be too drunk to notice. But you've saved the best!' 'Oh! Er – well – um – all part of the service, sir!' said the astonished caterer, and hurried over to Jesus. 'I don't know who you are or what you did,' he said, 'but you've saved my bacon today.'

It wasn't long before the word got around and the whole town was talking about Jesus. 'I can't understand it!' people would say, 'He's obviously a holy man – a religious man – but he really wants everyone to be happy.' Whenever Jesus heard people say it, he would answer that there's nothing strange in that. 'God wants everyone to be happy,' he would say, 'he just doesn't want you to make other people unhappy, in the process.'

Now there's really nothing strange about that, is there?

Based on John 2:1-11

Let's Chat

Some people think that religious people have to be unhappy,
but we know that when we're unhappy, God is too,
because he wants us to enjoy life.

We're Glad

Thank you, Jesus,
for wanting us to be happy.
Thank you for sharing life with us,
and for being there
when things go wrong.

We're Sad

Sometimes we're unhappy,
because we can't have
everything we want.
We get grumpy,
and we forget all the good things
we already have.
Then we upset others.
We're sorry.
Help us to be happy with what we've got.

Let's Pray for People

Jesus, our friend,
we know you want us to be happy,
but some people are very sad.
They think you don't approve of fun,
or laugh at jokes.
They think they shouldn't enjoy life.
So they make themselves unhappy,
and other people as well.
We pray for them:
help them to be happy,
and not to feel guilty.
Tell them that you love life,
and want them to enjoy it, too!

WELL, WELL, WELL!

*J*esus and his friends were out for a walk, and his friends were not very happy. 'I don't know why he's brought us this way,' grumbled Thomas, 'It's really a very rough area.' 'You're right,' said Philip, 'my mum always told me to stay away from this place. The people can't be trusted.' 'Mine said that, too,' said Matthew, 'there's a very high crime rate here, you know.' Jesus could hear them, but he just kept on walking, until they came to a well. Then he said, 'This is a good place to stop – let's have a picnic.' 'He must be barmy!' thought Peter, 'We haven't even got any food.' Jesus knew what he was thinking. 'There are some shops not far away,' he said, 'why don't you go and buy some food?' 'What, go in there?' said Thomas. 'Not on my own, I won't.' 'I meant all of you,' said Jesus, 'I'll be all right here.' Jesus' friends weren't at all sure about that. 'We can't leave him here on his own,' said Matthew, 'You know what Jesus is like, he'll talk to anybody and round here that's not a good idea.' 'That's true,' said Judas, 'he's so soft, he tries to be friends with some very doubtful people.' Peter interrupted: 'You mean, people like swindlers and thieves?' Matthew blushed, and Judas said, 'You said you weren't going to mention that again!' 'I know,' said Peter, 'but you did rather ask for it! Come on, Jesus can look after himself.'

So the disciples went away to buy some food while Jesus sat down at the well. 'It's really rather silly,' thought Jesus, 'here I am feeling thirsty, there's a well full of water and I've got nothing to get at it with!' Just as he was thinking that, a woman came up, with a cup in one hand and a bucket in the other, to get some water. 'I wonder if you could give me a drink from your cup?' asked Jesus. The woman, whose name was Becky, looked him up and down, very suspiciously. 'You're not from these parts, are you?' she asked, 'You're from the other side of the hill. I thought people like you didn't talk to people like me.' 'Why ever not?' asked Jesus. 'We're different,' said Becky, 'we have different ideas about life, and about God – we don't even worship God in the same place. You go to one kind of church and I go to another. If your friends knew you were talking to me – let alone asking me for a favour – they'd be very cross with you.' 'Yes,' said Jesus, 'I suppose they would. But all I'm asking for is a cup of water.' 'All you're asking for!' said Becky, 'Don't you realise that water's very precious around here?' 'Why?' asked Jesus. Becky couldn't believe her ears. 'Because we'd die without it, that's why!' she said. 'Really!' said Jesus, 'I suppose you call this living, do you, having to keep to your own side of the hill, and afraid to be seen talking to someone from the other side? What kind of life do you call that?' 'It's not much,' answered Becky, 'but it's all there is'. 'Well, that's where you're wrong,' said Jesus. 'people don't have to be enemies, just because they're different – and if we all learn to love one another, then that really would be living!' 'Oh yes?' said Becky. 'And I suppose you're the one who could give me this wonderful life, are you?' 'Got it in one!' said Jesus. 'Why don't you go and get your husband, so that I can tell him about it, too?' 'I haven't got a husband,' she said. 'Not at the moment,' said Jesus, 'but you've had quite a few, haven't you? Tell you what, go and get the man you're living with.' 'How on earth did you know about that?' asked Becky, but before Jesus could reply the disciples came into view, trudging back with the food they had bought.

'There you are,' said Matthew, 'I told you this would happen if we left him on his own – he's got talking to one of those dreadful women from the neighbourhood.'

'Well,' said Judas, 'I'm glad I took the purse with me – at least she couldn't get at any of our money.' John snorted angrily: 'You can talk about that,' he said, 'I've seen you with your hand in the purse when you thought no-one was looking.' Judas was really angry. 'You apologise for that, or I'll flatten you!' he bellowed at John. 'Oh do shut up, you two,' said Philip, 'none of us is perfect, and the least we can do is try to get along together.' 'Anyway,' said Peter, 'Jesus seems to have survived. She's just a woman like any other – people haven't got two heads around here, you know.'

As the disciples got closer, Becky said to Jesus, 'I'd better go, before your friends give you a hard time.' 'No need for that,' said Jesus, but Becky insisted. 'I'll go and tell my friends about you!' she said.

So off she went, back to her neighbours and her family. 'I've just met the most amazing man,' she said, 'from the other side of the hill.'

Her friends were horrified. 'From the other side of the hill?' they asked, 'Surely you didn't talk to him – you can't trust those people, you know.'

'That's funny,' said Becky, 'that's what his friends were saying about us. But he's really worth meeting. He knew all about me, even though he hadn't met me.'

'Oh well,' said her neighbour, Judy, 'if he knew all about you, and he's from the other side of the hill, he won't talk to you again, will he?' 'Yes he will,' said Becky, 'and he'll talk to you, as well. Please come and meet him.'

Eventually, Judy agreed to go back with her, even though she didn't want to, and the rest of the neighbours went as well, to keep an eye on them! When they met Jesus, they were amazed. 'He's not like other people!' they said. 'He accepts us just as we are.' Then they started talking to Jesus' friends, and it all finished up with everyone talking to each other, and they all forgot completely about which side of the hill everybody came from!

Well, well, well!

Based on John 4:5-42

Let's Chat

Are you afraid of some people just because they're different?
(Sometimes we're right to be afraid of people,
but for better reasons!)

We're Glad

We're glad, Jesus,
that people aren't all the same.
Thank you for showing us
how to love one another,
and not be afraid.

We're Sad

Jesus, we're sorry for being unkind
to people who are different from us.
They may believe different things
go to different kinds of churches,
like different kinds of food,
and have different ideas about life,
but you love them all.
Help us to love them too,
and help us to see that to them
it's we who are peculiar!

Let's Pray for People

We pray for all people who are lonely,
or who are angry,
because of the way other people treat them.
We pray for people who are afraid of others,
just because they're different.
We pray for ourselves.

THE BIGGEST PICNIC IN HISTORY

S am was well-known in his neighbourhood, with his curly hair (which looked as though he never brushed it!), his freckles and a big grin that never seemed to leave his face. He was the sort of boy who always wants to be where the action is. If there was anything exciting going on, you could bet Sam would be there! Sam also loved listening to stories. It didn't really matter what they were about – he just enjoyed sitting listening to them. So of course when he heard that the greatest storyteller ever was in the area, he wanted to go and listen. The storyteller's name was Jesus and Sam had heard him before. No one could tell stories quite the way he did: they were about the kind of people and places everyone knew well, and he told them in such a way that you just couldn't help listening. So Sam was really excited. 'Mum! Mum! Jesus is here! Can I go and listen to him? Please let me go!' Well, Mum knew that she wouldn't get any peace until she said 'yes', but she didn't let Sam go just like that. 'Take some food with you,' she said, 'once you start listening to that Jesus fellow, you're likely to be there all day!' She was right. Once Sam got listening to a good story, he'd forget about everything – including going home for tea! So Mum gave him a packed lunch, and it was a good thing she did. Sam wasn't the only one who forgot about food when Jesus was around.

Jesus wasn't actually planning on telling any stories that day. He really wanted to rest, and to pray. So he said to his disciples, 'Let's find a quiet place, where we can rest.' 'We could go into the hills,' said Philip, one of his friends, 'but we'd better hurry – people have heard that you're around.' So they went away into the hills, and didn't tell anybody where they were going. Unfortunately, it was about as hard to keep a secret where Jesus lived as it is in . . .* and it wasn't long before just about everyone knew where Jesus was! Before long, the 'quiet place' was full of people – about five thousand of them! 'Well,' said Jesus, 'that's our peace and quiet gone for a burton!'

*The name of your town or village

114

Jesus spent a lot of time talking to people. He spent even more time listening to them – letting them tell him the things they were worried about, or happy about. He knew that often the thing people most need is for someone to listen to them. As time went by, he realised that the people would be hungry – he always remembered about what people needed, even when they forgot about it themselves! 'They will be hungry,' he said, 'and they haven't brought any food. Can we buy them any?'

'We can't afford all that!' said Philip.

Sam thought he'd better try to help, so he went to see Andrew, one of Jesus' friends. 'I've got some food,' he said, 'look, there are five bread rolls and a couple of fish.' Andrew didn't think that would be very helpful, but he didn't want to be unkind. 'Let's go to Jesus,' he said, 'and see what he says.'

'Well,' said Jesus, 'I think we can do something with this. Tell everyone to sit down, and we'll share out the food we have.'

Andrew and the others thought Jesus was being very hopeful – how could they share out that little bit of food among five thousand people? But they knew Jesus well, and they knew that he was full of surprises. 'Come on,' said Peter, 'let's do it. Andrew, you start over there, James and John go to that side, and Judas, you'd better come with me – where I can keep an eye on you.'

So they got the people to sit down and began to share out the food. Can you guess what happened? Everyone had enough to eat! And not only that – when they picked up all the bits that had been dropped on the grass, they had another twelve baskets full of food.

Of course, everyone was very happy and thought Jesus was just the person they'd been waiting for. 'He ought to be our king,' they said, 'he'd be a lot better than Herod.'

Jesus didn't want that at all. Palaces, fancy clothes and servants bowing and scraping weren't his cup of tea! So he turned to his friends and said, 'I think it's time to find that quiet place we were looking for!' As Jesus and his friends slipped away, Sam went home. 'Well?' asked Mum, when he got back, 'What stories did Jesus tell today?' 'Oh,' said Sam, 'he told a few good ones, but what was really exciting was what Jesus *did*!'

Don't you agree?

Based on John 6:1-14

Let's Chat
What have you eaten today?
What's your favourite food?

We're Glad

Thank you, God,
for our food.
We like lots of different things,
and we know that they all come
from you.
Thank you for our food.

We're Sad

Sometimes, we're greedy;
we eat more than we need.
Other times, we throw food away;
we waste it.
We know some people are hungry,
and we could help them
more than we do.
We're sorry.

Let's Pray for People

Jesus, give us the things we need,
and help us not to be greedy,
or wasteful.
Bless all the people who grow our food,
or pack it,
or bring it to us,
and help us to care for others
who don't have enough.
Amen.

LIVING IN GLASS HOUSES

J esus and his friends were walking through the town one day, when they heard a dreadful noise. There was shouting, screaming and lots of clatter. Everyone turned to look and see what it was. Then, out of one of the side streets came a large crowd of people, dragging a woman along with them. She was very frightened and kept screaming and shouting, begging them to let her go. 'I'm sorry,' she kept saying, 'I won't do it again.' 'Huh! We've heard that before!' shouted one of the men. 'Yes,' yelled someone else, 'you're always saying that, but you've gone too far – you're a rotten, bad person.'

Well, all the noise and the nastiness continued, as they dragged the woman across the square. Jesus was horrified. 'We've got to stop this,' he said, 'look what they're doing to that poor woman.' His friends weren't so sure. 'I'd be careful, if I were you, Jesus,' said Matthew, 'there may be a good reason for it.' 'There's never a good reason to treat anyone like that!' replied Jesus. 'You don't know that,' said Peter, 'you don't know what she's done.' 'Whatever she's done,' said Jesus, 'she's a human being and they shouldn't treat her like that.' 'Well,' said James, 'I'd keep out of it, if I were you. It's always best not to get involved.' Jesus wasn't at all pleased by that and was going to say something very stern to James but, by that time, the crowd were across the square and almost on top of them.

'What on earth do you think you are doing?' Jesus asked the leader of the mob. The man, a nasty vindictive character, called Josh, said, 'If it's got anything to do with you, we're going to give her what she deserves.' 'And what might that be?' asked Jesus. 'We're going to kill her!' came a voice from the crowd. 'Yes,' shouted another gleefully, 'we're going to throw stones at her until she's dead.'

Jesus looked around the crowd and saw that quite a lot of them already had stones in their hands. His friend, John, had noticed that too. 'You'd better keep out of this one, Jesus,' he whispered, 'I'm afraid some of those stones might come in our direction if you don't.' 'What?' Jesus said, 'And let them stone this woman to death? I'm not going to stand by and let that happen.'

The crowd were getting impatient. 'Come on,' someone shouted, 'let's get her outside the town and get on with it.' But Jesus still stood in the way. 'Why do you want to do this?' he asked, 'What has she done?' Josh grinned in an evil way. 'She's always breaking the law,' he said, 'and we're going to see that she gets punished for it.' 'Yes,' said the person next to him, 'no-one respects the law these days – so we're going to enforce it.' 'But who do you think you are?' asked Jesus. 'An honest respectable citizen,' said Josh, with a self-satisfied look. Actually, he wasn't anything of the sort, but he had never been caught, so he thought that was all right!

Jesus still stood in the way. His friends were really getting anxious. 'He's going the right way about getting himself killed along with her,' muttered James. 'Yes,' said John, 'and us with him!' 'He's standing up for what's right,' said Thomas, 'I vote we stick with him.' Jesus thought for a moment longer and then said, 'I'll tell you what. If there's anyone among you who has never done anything wrong – anything at all, no matter how tiny – if there's anyone like that here, they can throw the first stone.'

Well! You could have heard a pin drop! Josh knew that, whatever he said to other people, he wasn't really as good as all that. After a few moments' thought, he let go of his stone and it went clattering down the hill. Then someone else did the same, and then another and, before long, the square was filled with the sound of stones hitting the road and rolling down the hill. As they dropped their stones, people turned and walked away, looking very embarrassed.

Eventually, the only people left were Jesus, his friends, and the poor, frightened woman, who by now was sitting on the floor, crying. Jesus spoke to her. 'There doesn't seem to be anyone having a go at you any more,' he said. 'No,' sobbed the woman, 'they aren't.' 'Well,' said Jesus, 'I'm certainly not going to. Go on home. No-one will try to hurt you. Now you've got the chance to start again. You can be a different person from now on!' The woman was so confused, and so relieved, that she just ran home – she didn't even stop to say 'thank you' to Jesus!

'Well, Jesus,' said Philip, 'that was amazing! They just seemed to fade away after what you said to them.' 'It's not so surprising, really,' Jesus answered, 'when it comes to throwing stones at others, people always find that they're living in glass houses themselves!'

Based on John 8:3-11

Let's Chat
Isn't it easy to find out what's wrong with people.
But it's much better to look for what's good!

We're Glad

You love us, Jesus,
whatever we're like:
when we're good,
and when we're not.
Thank you for all the people we know;
thank you for everything that's good about them.
Help us to notice the good things
more than the bad.

We're Sad

We know we're not always kind.
We often think other people are worse than they are,
and that we are better than we really are.
Jesus, help us to see,
the good that's in others.
And when we start to say
how bad they are,
help us to remember
that we aren't perfect, either.

Let's Pray for People

Jesus, you love everybody.
We pray for people who think
that nobody loves them,
or who think that they are bad.
Help us to be kind to them.
Help us to show that we care,
and that you love them.

I CAN SEE!

L et me tell you about Tim. He was a very bright sort of person – the sort who usually does well at school and goes on to get a good job afterwards. Because he was good with words, some people said he could have been a good lawyer, if only he'd had the chance. But the trouble was, he never did have the chance. He came from quite a good home, and he wasn't afraid of hard work. So you may wonder why he grew up to be a beggar – no job, no chance of getting married, having children, or even having a home of his own. Every day, he sat in the streets, hoping people would feel sorry for him and put a bit of money in the bowl beside him.

Tim's problem was that he was blind. He'd been blind, ever since he was born. In those days, that meant he'd never been able to go to school and he couldn't get a job. The rest of him worked very well – his ears could hear, his nose could smell, his mouth could talk. It was just that his eyes couldn't see. And because of that one thing, everyone thought he was useless. Poor Tim!

One day, as Tim sat in the streets begging, Jesus and his friends walked past. Matthew looked at him and said, 'I wonder why he's blind.' 'His parents must have done something dreadful,' replied James, 'and God's punishing them.' 'It might have been him,' said John, 'perhaps he's the one who's being punished – after all, he's the one who's blind.' 'Why don't you ask Jesus?' suggested Peter, 'When it comes to questions about God, he's usually got the answers.' So they went and asked Jesus.

Now you might be surprised that people actually thought like that. Fancy thinking that God would make someone blind, to punish someone else! But in those days a lot of people thought that. So Jesus wasn't surprised when his friends asked him the question.

'You don't really think God would do that, do you?' He asked his friends, 'But as the man is blind, he can help us to see how much God loves people.'

Then Jesus did something very strange. He made some mud from the dust on the ground and went over to smear it on Tim's eyes. Tim was surprised. 'Hey!' he shouted, 'What do you think you're doing – leave me alone – gerroff!' 'Don't worry,' said Jesus, 'I'm not trying to hurt you. My name is Jesus and I want to help you to see.' Then he told Tim to go to a pond nearby and wash the mud off his eyes. Tim didn't need to be told twice – after all, how would you like having mud smeared on your face? So off Tim went to the pool and washed his face. When he wiped the water away from his eyes, he started shouting, 'Hey, everybody, I can see! I can see people and houses, and this must be a tree . . .' Tim was running all over the place, from one thing to another, full of excitement. 'What's that?' he asked a man who was passing. 'What, that?' said the man, 'It's a donkey of course – haven't you ever seen a donkey before?' and he went off, muttering. But of course that was the whole point – Tim hadn't seen a donkey before – or a camel, or a dog, or a flower, or even his own hands. Tim hadn't seen anything at all before – no wonder he was so excited.

After a little while, some important people heard the noise and came to see what it was all about. 'What's going on?' asked Paul, who was a lawyer and a council member, 'What's all the fuss about?' 'I can see! I can see!' shouted Tim, excitedly. 'Don't be silly,' said Paul, 'you're blind – I've seen you begging in the streets.' 'Yes,' said Tim, 'but I can see now! Look, I can see a donkey over there and there's a camel and . . .' 'All right, calm down,' said Paul, 'how did this happen?' 'Well, it was the funniest thing,' explained Tim, 'this man called Jesus . . .' Paul interrupted. 'Jesus?' he said, 'Did you say Jesus?' 'Yes,' said Tim, 'a man called Jesus – he put some mud on my eyes and told me to wash. I thought he was barmy, I don't mind telling you – but now I can see!' 'That trouble-maker again!' thought Paul, 'If this goes on, people will think that Jesus is more important than me.' Then he turned to Tim. 'You're a liar,' he said, 'you were never blind at all, were you? You just pretended to be to get easy money from people.' 'Don't be silly!' said Tim, 'The amount of money I got that way, I'd far rather have worked.' 'All right, I believe you,' said Paul, 'but this is the day of rest. So if Jesus healed you today he must be an evil man, mustn't he?' 'Evil? Evil?' yelled Tim, 'How can someone who helps people in this way be evil?' Then some other lawyers joined in. 'This Jesus can't have come from God,' they said, 'or we'd have known about him. We don't know who he is.' 'Well, there's a funny thing,' said Tim, laughing at them, 'you don't know who he is! Isn't it obvious who he is? He's a good man, sent by God – that's who he is. Even I can see that. You clever lot can't see what's right in front of your noses – and to think, people used to say that *I* was blind!'

So Tim believed from then on that Jesus was a special good person, whom God had sent, but the lawyers carried on saying that Jesus was bad. Whatever good things Jesus did, they just kept on saying what a dreadful, wicked person he was. But then, as Tim used to say, there's none so blind as those who will not see!

Based on John 9: 1-39

Let's Chat

Can you imagine being blind?
What would you miss seeing, most?

We're Glad

It's good to be able to see.
We can see flowers, and trees, and pictures.
Best of all, we can see each other.
We can see when people need us,
and that they love us.
Thank you Jesus,
for helping us to see.

We're Sad

We don't always see things.
Sometimes people are worried, or upset,
and we don't notice.
We just carry on as though everything's fine,
and we don't see
that for some people, it's not.
Jesus, when we're happy,
remind us about others.
And when we're sad,
don't let us forget that others are, too.

Let's Pray for People

Let's pray for people who can't see.
Help them to use other ways
– like hearing, or touching,
and help us to know
when they need a bit of help.

DEAD AND ALIVE AGAIN

N|ot everyone liked Jesus. There were some people who liked to think they were important, and they were afraid Jesus might get to be more important than they were. There were other people who didn't like what Jesus said. 'He wants us to be friends with bad people,' they would say, 'and with people who have skin diseases and horrible things like that.' So one day, some of these people (who thought they were good, but were really not very nice at all) took Jesus to court and said horrible things about him. They even managed to frighten the Judge, so that he wanted to get rid of Jesus, and sentenced him to death. After Jesus died, the bad people thought they'd won. 'That will teach people not to interfere in our religion,' said Jerry, one of the religious leaders. 'Yes,' said another, 'and it will stop all that stuff about God loving everybody – so now we can go on saying that God only loves people like us – and Jesus won't be here to argue about it.' 'I think we've done a good day's work, getting rid of him,' said Jerry.

What they didn't know, of course, was that they hadn't got rid of him at all! Jesus was killed on the Friday. Nothing happened on Saturday, because that was the rest day and people weren't allowed to work. Then on the Sunday, Mary Magdalene said to her friends, Joanna and another Mary, 'Let's go to Jesus' grave. At the very least, we could put some flowers on it.' Joanna wasn't sure. 'The government didn't like Jesus,' she said, 'won't they be watching his grave, to find out who his friends were?' But the other Mary said, 'They probably know about us, anyway. I agree with Mary – we should go and have a look.'

So there they were, very early on Sunday morning, going along to the grave where Jesus had been buried. When they got there, they found that the grave was empty. Then they found someone waiting there, who said, 'It's no good looking for Jesus here – he's alive again, so what would he be doing in a grave?' Well, Joanna and Mary were terrified! They didn't know what was going on, but they knew they didn't like it very much! So they ran off and didn't dare tell a single person what they had seen. Mary Magdalene stayed, though. What was said hadn't sunk in and she was still wondering what to do when she thought she saw the gardener. It was not really light yet and she couldn't see very well, but she thought he looked like quite a kind person. so she said to him, 'I've come to find the grave where they buried Jesus, but it's empty. What have you done with him?' Then the man said to her, in a very familiar voice, 'Mary!' It was Jesus! He was alive again! Mary called out, 'Teacher!' and went to grab hold of him, but Jesus stopped her. 'Don't cling on to me,' he said. 'you can't just hang on to the past. We've got new things to do, now!' 'What shall I do, then?' asked Mary. 'Go and find the others,' said Jesus, 'and tell them that I'm alive.' 'Shall I bring them back here?' asked Mary. 'Oh no!' replied Jesus, 'Don't do that. I'm not going to hang around in this place for ever – I've got work to do.' 'So where will they find you?' asked Mary. 'Where they always have,' said Jesus, 'out in the world. Wherever people are, there they'll find me.'

So Mary went running back and told the disciples what Jesus had said. 'He's alive,' she said, 'and no-one's ever going to be able to kill him again. He's going to be here forever, even when we can't see him, and he'll never leave us.'

And d'you know, she was quite right.

Based on the Passion and Resurrection Narratives

Let's Chat

Isn't it good knowing that Jesus is alive?

We're Glad

Thank you God,
for bringing Jesus back to life.
Thank you for promising
that he'll always be with us.

We're Sad

We're not always as good as we could be.
We don't actually kill people
when we're jealous of them,
but sometimes we hurt them,
or try to make them look silly.
And when we're unkind to them
we hurt Jesus as well.
We're sorry.
Please Jesus,
help us to be kinder
to one another.

Let's Pray for People

Let's pray for people who are sad,
because someone has died.
Loving God,
even though we believe in heaven,
it still hurts when people die.
We miss them,
and we wish we could have them still with us.
Help people who are sad,
because someone they love has died.
Help them to trust you,
and help us to understand them.

I'LL BELIEVE IT WHEN I SEE IT

A fter Jesus had come back from the dead, Mary Magdalene ran very fast, and told Jesus' friends all about it. 'He was as close to me as you are,' she said, 'I could see the nail-marks in his hands.' But none of the men believed it. 'I wish it were true,' said Philip, sadly. 'Old wives' tales,' grumbled Andrew, unkindly. James was quite rude. 'You're drunk!' he said. 'What, this early in the morning?' said Mary, 'Do me a favour! I tell you he's alive.' But whatever she said, Mary couldn't convince the friends of Jesus that she'd seen him. But then, as they were arguing, they suddenly found that Jesus was standing among them! They were terrified! They thought it must be a ghost – after all, the doors and windows were locked and he couldn't have come down the chimney, with the fire burning! Jesus smiled at them. 'Don't worry,' he said, 'I'm not a ghost. Here, come and take hold of my hand, just to prove that I'm real.' Very gingerly, Peter went up and took Jesus' hand. 'It's true!' he shouted. 'It really is him!' Then everyone just went wild! They all crowded round Jesus, trying to grab hold of him and asking lots and lots of questions. But Jesus stopped them. 'I'm not going to answer all the questions now,' he said, 'the important thing is that God has brought me back to life. Your job is to go and tell everybody that – not waste time trying to work out how he did it!' Then, all of a sudden, he was gone! This really was very difficult for his friends. They'd never been too sure what he was going to do next, before Jesus had been killed. But now, he seemed to be able to come and go as he liked and he was obviously going to be even more free, now. 'The fact is,' Peter said, 'no-one's ever been able to pin Jesus down, and we certainly can't now. He's not just alive, he's *free* as well!' As he was speaking, Thomas came in. He'd been out visiting his twin brother Jeremiah and had missed all of the drama. As he came into the room, he could tell that everybody was excited. 'What's going on?' he asked. 'Jesus has been here,' said John. 'He's alive,' said James. 'Pull the other one!' said Thomas. Well, you can't really blame him, can you? It must have sounded pretty unlikely! No matter what they said, they couldn't convince Thomas. 'I'll tell you what,' he said to them, 'if I can see him, and touch him, and touch the wounds on his body, then I'll believe he's alive. But until then, I won't believe a word of it!' 'Why?' asked Philip, 'Don't you trust us, your own friends?' 'Not a lot,' said Thomas, 'remember that time when you told me the easy way to count sheep?' 'What was that?' asked Mary Magdalene. 'Count the legs and divide by four!' said Andrew. 'And Thomas actually tried it!' said James and everyone laughed – except Thomas. 'Laugh if you like' he said, 'but you're not catching me out like that again. I'll believe it when I see it.' And with that, he went home.

Thomas didn't see the other friends again for a week. They were in the room where they usually met and were chatting away about this and that. Peter and Andrew were having an argument with James and John about what kind of bait was best for fishing nets and, in another corner, Philip was complaining to Matthew that the government had charged him too much tax, by mistake. Just as Matthew was saying, 'I'm not in that business any more of course, but I'll check your books if you like,' everything went quiet! Jesus had come into the room again, and Thomas was staring at him as though he'd seen a ghost – which he probably thought he had.

'Come here, Thomas,' said Jesus, 'I've something to show you.' Thomas went up to Jesus, and Jesus showed him the wounds where the nails had gone into his hands and feet, and where a soldier's spear had cut into his side. 'You see, Thomas, it really is true,' Jesus said, 'and I'm certainly no ghost, am I? Come and touch me, if you like, and you'll find that I'm real.' Thomas didn't need to touch Jesus – he knew then that Jesus really had come back from the dead. He was overjoyed. 'It's true!' he said, looking around him in amazement, 'My master – alive!' 'You've seen me,' Jesus said, 'and now you can believe. It's going to be harder for people who don't see me. You've got to go and help them.'

Some of the disciples used to tease Thomas after that, because he had doubted what they had told him. I expect he probably said, 'You've got no room to talk – you didn't believe it, either, when the women told you. You had to see before you believed, just like me.'

And of course, he would have been quite right, wouldn't he?

Based on John 20:24-29

Let's Chat

Some things are hard to believe aren't they? It depends upon
who it is that tells us, and how much we trust them.

We're Glad

We're glad you're alive, Jesus,
and even though we can't see you,
we know you're here,
because you help us
to love one another.
Thank you Jesus,
for loving us,
and for being here.

We're Sad

Sometimes, Jesus, when we're unkind,
other people find it hard to believe in you.
We're sorry.
Help us to be more like you,
so that other people will know
that you're alive.

Let's Pray for People

We're unkind to Thomas:
we call him 'Doubting Thomas'.
Perhaps we should call him 'Honest Thomas'!
We pray for people who are unsure
about what they believe.
Help them to be honest,
help others to understand,
and help us to be honest as well.

COME ON, COUGH UP!

B art was a very rich man. He was also very kind and often helped out other people who were in difficulties. Then one day, he went to see his accountant – a man called Matthew. 'I'm a little bit worried,' Matthew said, 'about the amount of money you've lent to some people.' 'Oh, don't worry about that,' replied Bart, 'I'll get it back one day.' 'Well, most of these people don't owe you very much, I suppose,' said Matthew, 'but there's one here – a chap called Joel – he owes you a million pounds!' 'Really?' said Bart in surprise, 'I hadn't realised it had mounted up that much.' 'Well that's what happens,' said Matthew, 'a lot of little bits soon add up to a very big chunk indeed! I think you ought to talk to him about it.'

So, when he went home, Bart sent a message to Joel, asking him to call in when he was passing. Joel was very worried. He knew he owed Bart a lot of money and he couldn't even begin to pay him back. 'I'd better go,' he thought, 'and see if I can get him to wait a bit longer.' So Joel went to see Bart. 'I just wonder whether you realise,' said Bart 'that you now owe me a million pounds?' 'Really? Is it as much as that?' asked Joel. 'I'm afraid it is,' said Bart. Joel got very frightened. 'I'll pay you back as soon as I can,' he pleaded, 'but please not just yet. One of my children is about to get married and my wife's been ill for a long time as you know. So I need every penny I can get – please don't ask for it back yet.' Bart felt very sorry for Joel. 'Look,' he said, 'I know you're having a hard time – and we're all very worried about your wife. To be honest, I don't really need the money – why don't we just forget about it?' 'You mean, forget about it for a few weeks?' asked Joel. 'No,' said Bart kindly, 'just forget about it. Don't worry about paying me back, ever.' Joel could hardly believe his ears! 'Do you really mean that?' he asked, 'Oh thank you ever so much. We're all really grateful to you.' And Joel went off, out of Bart's house and down the street, as though he was walking on air! He couldn't believe how generous Bart had been! 'I must find some way of showing how grateful I am,' he thought. 'Perhaps I could buy him a present, if I only had some money.'

Just then, he saw his neighbour, Nick, walking towards him. 'Aha!' he thought, 'Nick owes me fifty pounds – that would buy a nice thank you present for Bart.' 'Hello, Nick,' he said. 'Hello, Joel,' said Nick, 'isn't it a lovely day?' 'Yes,' said Joel, 'Er, Nick, you know that fifty pounds you owe me – I'm afraid I need it back.' Nick was most upset. 'I'm sorry,' he said, 'but I haven't got it. Please be patient with me – my father died last week and I've got the funeral to pay for. I'll pay you back as soon as I can, though.' Joel got very angry. He even grabbed Nick by the throat! 'Give me my money!' he shouted at him. 'Come on, cough up!' Nick was certainly coughing all right! He though he was going to choke to death.

'All right,' he spluttered, 'if it's so important – but I'll have to borrow it from somebody.' 'I don't care what you do,' said Joel roughly, 'Just get it.' Then he went on his way, thinking, 'Won't Bart be pleased when I give him his present?'

Nick tried to borrow the money to pay Joel back. He couldn't find anyone with that much money to spare, until someone said, 'Why don't you go to Bart? He'll lend it to you.' 'Good idea,' said Nick, and went off to Bart's house.

'Of course, I'll lend you the money,' said Bart, 'Do you mind telling me what you want it for?' And then Nick told him the whole story, not realising that Bart and Joel knew each other! 'What!' shouted Bart, enraged, 'Do you mean he actually attacked you over a fifty pound debt? You leave Joel to me – I'll deal with him.' Then he sent a message, asking Joel to come and see him.

Joel was puzzled. He couldn't think why Bart should want to see him. After all, he didn't owe him anything any more, did he? Still, it would be nice to go and have a chat, he thought. So he trotted along to Bart's house. Now a few days earlier, he would have knocked politely on the door and waited to be invited in. But now, of course, it was different – or so he thought. So he marched up to the door, flung it open and breezed in. 'Wotcher, Bart,' he said, 'what's new?' Bart's reply nearly knocked him over. 'Get out and knock!' Bart bellowed, 'And don't come in until I tell you.' Joel was scared stiff! He ran outside and closed the door. It took him quite a few moments to pluck up the courage to knock.

Inside the room, Bart heard the knock, and recited a little rhyme to himself:

'One, two, three, four,
let him sweat a little more.
Five, six, seven, eight,
bet he's getting in a state!'

Then he shouted, 'Come in – don't keep me waiting!'

Joel went in. 'Wh-wh-what do you w-w-want me for?' he asked. 'What's this I hear about you being unkind to Nick?' asked Bart. 'I only asked him if he'd give me what he owes me,' said Joel. 'Asked him? Jolly near throttled him, from what I hear!' Bart corrected him. 'And him recently bereaved as well!' 'I only did it because I wanted to buy you a present,' said Joel, 'I wanted to show you I was grateful.' 'So you show me how grateful you are by bullying one of my friends, do you,' roared Bart 'and to think I let you off a million pounds! Well, you'd better pay me back by next week.' 'What, all of it?' gulped Joel. 'Every single penny!' said Bart. 'And if you haven't got it, I've got a nice damp dungeon waiting for you.' 'I'll get it, I'll get it!' babbled Joel. 'Well don't get it by threatening any more people,' said Bart, 'or it will be worse for you!'

Poor old Joel. If only he'd been as kind to Nick as Bart was to him, he'd never have got into all that trouble, would he?

Based on Matthew 18:21-34

Let's Chat

Can you remember someone being really generous to you?

We're Glad

Thank you God,
for being so good to us,
even though we don't deserve it.
Thank you for people who are kind,
and who don't ask us
to repay their kindness.
But help us to do it anyway,
by being kind to other people.

We're Sad

We're not always kind.
Sometimes we're quite cruel,
even though other people are kind to us.
We're sorry, Jesus,
help us to remember
how much you've forgiven us,
and that we should forgive others, too.

Let's Pray for People

Some people are very unhappy,
because they can't forgive others.
They bear grudges,
and they keep reminding themselves
of how they've been hurt.
Help them to learn
that by forgiving people,
they help make themselves happier, too.

EVERYONE GETS THE SAME

O ne day, Jesus wanted to show people what God was like. So he told them a story a little bit like this:

Jack was a farmer and he was well-known and well-liked in his village. Whenever anyone was looking for a job, they would hope Jack might give them one, because he was a good man to work for. 'He's fair, is old Jack,' the people used to say, 'he pays a fair day's wage for a fair day's work.'

In the harvest season, people without jobs used to go and wait in the market square, hoping that Jack, or one of the other farmers, would come and ask them to work. One particular day, Jack needed an extra worker to help with the harvest and so he went into the market place. When he got there, he found several men waiting. 'What's you name?' he asked the first one. 'My name's Ben,' was the reply, 'and I'm looking for work for the day.' 'Good,' said Jack, 'because I'm looking for a worker! Are you any good at harvesting corn?' 'Oh, I've done a lot of that,' said Ben, 'what will you pay?' 'I'll pay you twenty pounds for the day,' said Jack. 'Fair enough,' said Ben, and they went off together.

Ben worked really hard that day, but at about lunch time, he realised that he was going to need some help. 'I won't be able to get all this corn in today,' he said to Jack, 'and they say there's a storm coming tonight.' Jack looked at the sky and said, 'You know, I think you're right. I'll get someone else to help you.' So off he went, back to the market place. 'What's your name?' he asked the first man he came to. 'I'm Joe,' said the man, 'and I'm getting a bit desperate – nobody seems to want any work doing today and I need the money to get myself a warm coat for the winter.' 'I need a worker,' said Jack, 'and I'll pay you twenty pounds if you come and work in my field.' 'Terrific!' said Joe, 'I'll come straight away.' So they went back together and Joe got straight to work, alongside Ben. When it got to about three o'clock, Joe said to Ben, 'You know, we're not going to get finished today, at this rate.' 'No,' said Ben, 'We really could do with some more help.' So Jack went off to the market place again. There was a woman standing there, looking very fed up indeed! 'No-one seems to want any work doing today,' she said, 'this recession's really bad! I'll never get my garden fence mended if I don't earn a day's pay soon.' 'What do you do?' asked Jack. 'Anything I'm asked to,' said the woman, 'but I'm best at farm work – I grew up on a farm, and I'm used to it.' 'Well, you'd better come with me,' said Jack, 'what's your name?' 'Dinah,' she said. 'Well, Dinah,' said Jack, 'if you don't mind working for me, I'll give you twenty pounds for the rest of the day.' Dinah thought that sounded good, so they went back together, and she set to work in the fields.

At the end of the day, Jack called his foreman and said, 'Larry, I want you to take this money and pay the casual workers. Start with the one who came last. So Larry went out and called Ben, Joe and Dinah over. 'Thank you for your help, Dinah,' he said, 'Jack's really pleased with the work you've done. Here's your twenty pounds.' 'Thank you very much,' said Dinah, 'if you need me tomorrow, I'll be in the market square again.' Ben nudged Joe and whispered, 'This is all right. If she got twenty pounds for just a few hours, I bet he'll pay us a bonus.' 'So I should hope,' said Joe, 'after all we were here in the heat of the day – she just did a couple of hours in the afternoon!' Larry came over to Joe. 'Thank you,' he said, 'you've done a really good job today. Here's your twenty pounds.' 'Twenty pounds!' exclaimed Joe, 'What do you call that?' 'I'm sorry,' said Larry, 'I thought Jack said you were each to have twenty pounds. Have I made a mistake?' 'Someone has!' replied Joe, 'That Dinah woman got twenty pounds – and she'd only worked a couple of hours.'

Jack had heard the row (most of the village must have heard it, the way Joe was shouting!) and he came over. 'What's wrong?' he asked. 'I'll tell you what's wrong,' said Ben, 'you've given that woman who started in the afternoon the same as you promised Joe and me. That's not fair. Joe should get more than that and I should get more than him, because I worked longest.' 'I don't know what you're so upset about,' said Jack, 'you're going to get what we agreed – twenty pounds.' 'But you've given her the same,' yelled Ben, 'and she hasn't done as much work, so she doesn't deserve as much pay.' 'I never said that she deserved it,' said Jack, 'I don't care what she deserves – I'm only interested in what she needs – and she's got bills to pay, just the same as you have.' 'Well!' said Joe, 'Everybody around here says that you're a fair man – they're wrong.' 'Yes, they are,' said Jack, 'because I'm not trying to be fair – I'm trying to be generous, and that's not the same thing at all. Is it so bad to be generous, with my own money?'

As Ben and Joe left, with twenty pounds each, Larry said, 'I think you've upset those two.' 'I know,' said Jack, 'because they thought I should care about what they deserved, and I care more about what they need. If I'd been fair, and just given what they deserved Joe couldn't have his new coat for the winter, and Dinah's garden fence would have to stay broken. How would that have helped Ben to feel better? People can be very silly at times!'

As it was, Joe got his coat, Dinah got her fence repaired and after a while all the jealousy was forgotten. Joe, Dinah and Ben became good friends and often went to work for Jack together. Gradually people stopped saying that Jack was 'a very fair man'. Instead, they used to say, 'He's very generous, you know,' which was really much nicer, wasn't it?

Based on Matthew 20:1-16

Let's Chat

What kind of things do we all need –
food, warmth, smiles and hugs?

We're Glad

Thank you, Jesus,
for knowing what we need,
and for caring about it.
Thank you for being not only fair,
but generous!

We're Sad

Sometimes, Jesus, we're not nice to people,
because we think they don't deserve it.
But you told us to be especially nice
to people we think are bad,
or who are not nice to us.
We're sorry that we haven't been
as generous as you.
Forgive us,
and help us to do better.

Let's Pray for People

Loving God,
you care about people.
We pray for people who need clothes
people who need houses,
people who need to be loved.
Help us to notice them,
and to do something to help.

WHAT HAVE YOU DONE WITH MY MONEY?

D avid was a very rich man and he had lots of people working for him. One day, when he was going away, he called three of them and said, 'I'm going to give you each some of my money and I want you to use it for me, to keep the business going while I'm away. Let's start with you, Chloe.' Chloe was very excited. She'd always wanted the chance to do some business herself. 'What shall I do, boss?' she asked. 'What are you good at?' responded David. 'I can grow things,' said Chloe, 'perhaps I'll open a garden centre.' 'Sounds like a good idea to me,' said David, 'here's ten thousand pounds to start you off.' Chloe went away, very excited, and David went to the next servant. 'Well, Barney,' he said, 'what would you do with five thousand pounds?' Barney could hardly believe his luck! 'I could start a catering business,' he said, 'whenever people get married, or have a party, they have to get people in from the next town. I think a catering business would do well.' 'Good!' said David, 'Here's your money, go and get on with it.' So off went Barney, muttering to himself, 'I'll need cooking pots, jugs, plates – lots of plates – and I'll need . . .' David could hear him muttering away excitedly, all the way down the passage. Then David turned to the third servant. 'Phil,' he said, 'I'll give you two thousand pounds; what will you do?' Phil hadn't got a clue. In fact, he was scared to death at the very idea. 'David's a good businessman,' he thought, 'if I muck things up, he's going to be really angry with me!' But he didn't dare say that to David, so he just mumbled something about having to think about it. 'You make sure you do,' said David, and gave him the money. Then David went off on his journey. 'Don't forget,' he said to all of them, 'I'll want to see what you've done when I get back.'

Chloe went out straight away and bought a piece of land. She got some builders in to put up fences and to build her a potting shed and a tool shed, and she went and bought all kinds of tools, seeds, bulbs – everything you can think of. Phil watched her and thought to himself, 'Ten thousand pounds won't last long at that rate. She'll have lost the lot before David comes home.'

Barney went out looking for a shop. He found one for sale near the town centre. It wasn't very big, but he thought, 'This will be enough to begin with.' Then he got the builders in. 'I'll need a food store over there,' he told them, 'and a large oven in that corner.' He sent for a carpenter as well. 'Lots of cupboards and shelves, please,' he said. Then he went out to see the potter and ordered cooking pots and dishes, and lots of plates and cups. Phil watched him doing all this and thought, 'He'll soon have wasted all that money, and then he'll be in real trouble.'

Phil couldn't think what to do with the money David had given him. 'Whatever I do will be bound to fail,' he thought, gloomily. Eventually, he went out into his back garden, dug a hole and buried it all! 'There!' he thought, 'I won't make any profit, but at least I won't have wasted it, like those other two are doing.'

Meanwhile, signs were being put up all over the town, saying things like: *Get your Geraniums from Chloe's* and *Come to Chloe's for Cucumbers*. There were some other signs, too, that said things like: *Let Barney Cater for You*, and *Barney's Better Caterers*. (Don't confuse this with the other BBC, though, will you?) Very soon, people were coming from all over the place to buy flowers from Chloe, or wedding cakes from Barney. In fact, they had to make the High Street one way to prevent camel jams!

Of course, after a few months, David came back. Chloe got someone to look after the garden centre and Barney put a sign on his door saying: *Closed for the day, please try tomorrow*. Then they both went to meet David. Phil, who was not at all happy, went into his garden and dug up the money he'd buried. Somehow, he knew he was going to be in trouble!

'Well,' said David, 'what have you done while I've been away?' Chloe stepped forward, proudly. 'You remember giving me ten thousand pounds?' she said, 'Well I've done what I said I would, and the garden centre's done really well. I've got your ten thousand pounds here, and another ten thousand as well.' 'Well done, Chloe,' said David. 'I'm really pleased with you, and I'm going to make you a partner in my business.' Then David turned to Barney. 'Well, Barney,' he said, 'how's the catering business?' 'Very good, thank you,' said Barney, 'I've got the five thousand pounds you gave me, and I've made you another five thousand as well.' 'This is really good!' exclaimed David, 'I'm going to make you a partner in my business, as well.' Then he turned to Phil. 'You weren't sure what to do, were you,' he said, 'what did you decide on in the end?' Phil was very frightened, and ashamed. 'Er . . . um . . . ah . . . that is, well, you see you're such a good businessman – and I knew you'd be angry if I lost your money, so I decided not to take any chances.' David was not looking happy. 'Out with it,' he said, 'what have you done with my money?' 'N-n-nothing, sir,' stammered Phil, 'I kept it safe for you. Here it is, the very same two thousand pounds you gave me.' 'Is that all you've done?' asked David. 'At the very least you could have put it in the bank for me, and got some interest.' 'I was frightened,' said Phil, 'I knew you expected a lot of me, and I was sure I'd fail.' David was really angry. 'That's no excuse for doing nothing!' he shouted, 'I wouldn't have minded if you'd tried, and got it wrong – even if you'd lost it all, at least you'd have tried. But not even to try at all – there's no excuse for that.' Then he turned to Chloe. 'Could you use another couple of thousand?' he asked. 'You bet I could,' said Chloe, 'I could open a refreshment room.' 'Yes,' said Barney, 'and I could do the catering for you.' So everyone was very happy – except poor old Phil, that is. If only he'd realised that there's no shame in failing – only in not even trying!

Based on Matthew 25:14-30

Let's Chat

What are you good at? Can you make other people happy?
That's the best gift God gives to us!

We're Glad

Thank you, God,
for trusting us.
We can all do something
to make the world a better place.
Help us to trust you,
and to use whatever you've given us
to make other people happy.

We're Sad

There are lots of things we can do
to help other people:
we can smile,
we can listen,
we can cheer them up if they're sad,
all sorts of things.
But sometimes we don't do them,
because we're afraid of getting things wrong.
But even if we did,
at least they'd know we'd tried!
We're sorry, Jesus,
help us to trust you more.

Let's Pray for People

Some people are always nervous,
afraid of getting things wrong.
So they never really enjoy life,
they miss so much!
We pray for them, Jesus,
give them confidence,
and help us to show them
how important they are to us.

NEIGHBOURS

O ne day, someone asked Jesus, 'You know that law that says we're supposed to love God and love our neighbours?' 'Yes,' said Jesus, 'I know it.' 'Well,' said the man, 'just who exactly is my neighbour?' So Jesus told a story, rather like this one.

There was once a young man called Stephen. He was a quiet sort of person. He didn't like sports and that kind of thing very much, but he loved to read. One day, he said to his mother, 'I'm going out for the day – I want to go to the library at Jericho, to look at some books.' 'Jericho?' said his mother, 'Why can't you use the library here in Jerusalem?' 'Because they haven't got the special books I want, Mother,' explained Stephen patiently. 'Well, you're not going on that road on your own, are you?' asked Mother anxiously, 'People get mugged along there.' 'Oh, don't be silly!' said Stephen, 'I can look after myself – you really do make a fuss!' And out he went, down the road from his house, left at the butcher's shop, down the hill, right at the carpenter's workshop, and he was on the Jericho Road.

Stephen's mother was right to be worried. There were lots of hills and caves along the lonely road, and bandits hid out in them, waiting to rob people who went that way. One of them, a very nasty man called Barabbas (whom you may have heard of before), looked out over the stone he was hiding behind, and saw Stephen coming. 'Hey, fellas!' he called out, but not loudly enough for Stephen to hear, 'There's some mug here walking on his own – let's get him!' And so, without any warning at all, Stephen suddenly found himself surrounded by half a dozen large and very violent men. He tried his best, of course. He caught Barabbas with the end of a stick and made his nose bleed, and he kicked another one very hard on the shins. But it was no good. Very soon, poor Stephen was lying on the road, with his face cut, his nice clothes torn and bloodstained, and all his money gone. He couldn't move – not even crawl to the side of the road, out of the hot sun. He just had to lie there. Then he heard someone coming. 'I hope it's not another robber,' he thought. The footsteps got closer, and a man looked down at Stephen. He was a priest – Stephen knew that from the way he was dressed. 'Oh, good!' thought Stephen, 'He's sure to help me.' 'What's happened to you?' the priest asked. Stephen thought that was a silly question and nearly said, 'I was out fishing and my boat sank,' but thought he'd better not be rude. 'I've been mugged,' he said, 'can you help me?' 'Terribly sorry, old chap,' said the priest, 'but you're all covered in blood, and I'm just going to a service, so I mustn't get dirty. But don't worry, there'll be someone else along. God bless you.' And he hurried away.

Stephen could think of a few things to shout after him, but he decided to save his strength. Then he heard someone else coming. This time it was a different kind of minister. 'Well,' thought Stephen, 'perhaps he'll help me.' 'I say,' said the minister, 'have you had an accident?' 'No,' said Stephen, 'I've been mugged.' 'Oh dear!' exclaimed the minister, 'Are the robbers still around?' 'I don't know,' said Stephen, 'but can you help me?' He was too late. The minister wasn't taking any chances and had already scuttled off along the road, glancing nervously around him. Stephen was really worried now. The sun was hot and people had died on that road after being robbed. It really looked as though he would be the next. Then someone else came along and had a look. 'Oh, no!' thought Stephen, 'I know him. It's Tom, that Samaritan who sells second-hand donkeys.' Well, you could understand Stephen being worried. After all everyone knew that Samaritans hated Jews, and everyone also knew that you couldn't trust a second-hand donkey salesman. But Stephen was in for a surprise.

'Dear me,' said Tom, 'you do look in a bad way. Don't worry – I'll soon get you somewhere more comfortable.' 'You mean you're going to help me?' asked Stephen. 'Of course I am,' replied Tom. 'But what about the robbers?' said Stephen. 'Oh,' said Tom, 'I expect they're long gone by now, and if they're not, they'd probably get me even if I didn't stop to help. Now stop talking, and let me get on.' He rummaged around and found a bottle of wine. 'Hey,' said Stephen, 'this is no time for social drinking.' 'I'm not going to drink it,' said Tom, 'I'm going to clean your wounds with it; the water's not very good in these parts – full of dreadful chemicals, not at all natural!' Tom hadn't got a first-aid kit, like you might have in your car; so he took his shirt off and tore it up to make bandages so that he could clean and dress Stephen's wounds. Then he said, 'D'you think you could get onto my donkey, if I helped you? We need to get to a hotel.' 'Hotel?' said Stephen, 'I can't afford any hotel – and anyway, my mother will be worried.' 'You certainly can't go home like that,' said Tom, 'and the hotel's the only place for miles. Let me take you there and I'll see you're taken care of. It won't cost you anything and I'll take a message to your mother.'

Tom did just as he said he would. He took Stephen to the hotel and told them to look after him there until he was well. 'I'm often along this road,' he said, 'I'll pay you when I come back.' Then he went over to Stephen. 'Now don't you worry,' he said, 'I'll tell your mother you're all right and you'll be home in a few days. And don't fret about the hotel bill – I've told them I'll pay it.'

Stephen could not believe what was happening. He kept on saying 'thank you' so often that Tom went quite red! Then, as Tom was leaving, Stephen called out, 'Just a minute, can I ask you a question.' 'If you like,' said Tom, 'what is it?' 'Are you *really* a Samaritan?' asked Stephen. 'Yes,' answered Tom, 'I really am.' There was a silence, and then Stephen, looking really puzzled, said, 'And are you *really* a second-hand donkey salesman?'

Based on Luke 10:30-35

Let's Chat

Sometimes we get help from people we don't expect.
Have you ever been surprised like that?

We're Glad

Thank you, Jesus,
for lovely surprises,
when people we thought were bad
turn out to be good.
Thank you, Jesus,
for lovely surprises.

We're Sad

Jesus, we say we're your friends,
so people expect us to be friendly.
Sometimes they get bad surprises from us.
They think we'll be kind and we're cruel,
or they expect us to be generous
and we're selfish.
Then we let them down,
and ourselves,
and we let you down too.
We're sorry, Jesus,
help us to be good friends,
and good neighbours.

Let's Pray for People

Some people feel lonely,
as though they haven't got any good neighbours.
Help them to know that you love them,
and teach us to be good neighbours.

LET'S HAVE A PARTY!

M ike and Sarah were very well off. They had a beautiful big house, with a huge garden and, now that Mike had retired, they had a lot of spare time. They loved that – they used to go walking together in the fields, saying hello to the farm workers; sometimes they'd just enjoy sitting on the patio outside their house, watching the sunset. And something else they loved to do was to throw dinner parties. They were well-known for them. There was always lots and lots of food – just imagine all your most favourite foods piled up on a big table, (such as . . .) and that's what Mike and Sarah's parties were like. The table would be set with all the best pots and dishes and there would be vases of flowers at each end and in the middle. They always had a band, who would play softly during the meal, so that people could enjoy a good chat as they ate. Then, when the meal was over, the band would strike up some dance music. The next house was a long way away and they could make a noise without disturbing anybody. Their parties were the talk of the neighbourhood. If you were invited to one it was a great honour, and people used to say that only a very special kind of fool would ever refuse an invitation to a party at Mike and Sarah's place.

One evening, Sarah said to Mike, 'I've been thinking, it's a long time since we had a party.' 'You're right,' replied Mike, 'it's really about time we had another.' 'Let's make a list of guests,' said Sarah, 'it will be so nice to see some old friends again.' 'We can invite Joe and Elizabeth,' said Mike. 'That's a good idea,' said Sarah, 'and we really must invite Tim and Anna, and what about Eli, the chap who's just moved here from Bethany?' So the invitations were sent out:

Mike and Sarah
request the pleasure of the company of
Joe and Elizabeth
on Sunday night at 7.30

Other invitations were sent out to Tim and Anna, and to Eli. Then Mike and Sarah began to prepare the food. The big stone oven was working overtime that week! At the same time, Mike and Sarah were out in the garden gathering in all kinds of fruit. 'We'll have a fruit punch,' said Sarah. 'Yes,' said Mike, 'but be careful how much wine you put into it – not everyone's used to your punches!'

By Sunday night, all the food was ready and the table was set out. As usual, apart from the food, there were candles and flowers on the table and the Bethany Blues Band were playing gently at one end of the room. Mike and Sarah were really excited – it had been some time since the last party. But gradually when no-one came, they started getting worried. 'I hope they haven't forgotten,' said Sarah, 'it would be such a shame to waste all this food.' 'I'll go and check,' said Mike. So he went out, got onto his horse and rode off to Joe and Elizabeth's place. Elizabeth answered the door and looked very embarrassed. 'I'm sorry,' she said, 'but we've just bought that bit of land next door to our garden and it's absolutely covered in weeds! I'm afraid we're going to have to go and work on it. You do understand, don't you?' Mike wasn't very pleased. 'I wish you'd told us before,' he said, 'we've gone to a lot of trouble.' Then he went off to find Tim and Anna. 'I really am dreadfully sorry,' said Tim, 'but we've just bought this lovely new puppy, and we can't leave him all on his own, can we? I hope you haven't gone to too much trouble.' 'Yes,' replied Mike, '*much* too much trouble!' And he went and got back on his horse. 'Eli's probably forgotten,' he thought to himself, 'I expect he'll ride back with me.' But when he got to Eli's house, there wasn't a sign of him anywhere. Then one of the neighbours called out, 'Eli's away – he got married this morning and he's off on his honeymoon. Won't be back for a week.'

When Mike got home, Sarah was as angry as he was. 'D'you mean to tell me that they let us do all this work and didn't really want to come at all?' she said, 'Well, we've got to find someone who can eat this food; it mustn't be wasted.'

'I know!' said Mike, 'If the people who were invited don't appreciate our cooking, let's invite those who will!' 'Like who?' asked Sarah. 'Let's go out into the streets,' said Mike, 'and find all the homeless people, all the people nobody likes, and let's invite them!' 'What a wonderful idea!' exclaimed Sarah, 'They'll appreciate a good party, even if our boring friends don't!' So that's what they did. They went out onto the streets and found people who hadn't got homes, or who couldn't afford food, and they invited them all in. Before long, the house was full of people eating and laughing and singing and dancing. 'Well!' said Sarah, 'this is a bit different from the kind of party we thought of. No posh clothes, or airs and graces – just people who appreciate a good party.' 'Yes,' said Mike, 'even the band are enjoying it more than usual – just listen to how they're playing!'

Just then, there was a knock at the door and there stood Joe and Elizabeth. 'We felt so sorry for you,' said Joe, as they swept in, 'that we decided to put off the weeding and come here. After all what are friends for?' Before Mike could answer, the new guests had arrived in the dining room. 'Good grief!' screeched Elizabeth, 'What on earth are all *these* people doing here?' 'Enjoying themselves, actually,' said Sarah, 'you know, they really know how to get stuck in to a good party. Why don't you join them?' 'Not on your life!' replied Elizabeth. 'Come on Joe, we're going home!'

So Joe and Elizabeth went home, but the party continued well into the night. There had never been such a party! No-one wanted it to end. As they left the guests all said, 'When's the next party going to be?' 'Just as soon as we can organise it,' smiled Sarah. 'Too right!' said Mike, 'I've never enjoyed anything so much!'

Based on Luke 14:15-24

Let's Chat

Do you like parties? What do you do at them?

We're Glad

Loving God,
thank you for fun,
for our family
and the things we enjoy together.
Help us to make each other happy.

We're Sad

Sometimes people go to a lot of trouble
to make us happy,
and we hurt them.
We're sorry, Jesus,
help us to be more careful
about other people's feelings.

Let's Pray for People

Some people are so sad,
and never really enjoy life.
They don't notice
the good things others do.
Other people spend lots of time
trying to make others happy,
and then feel as though they don't care.
We pray for them.
Help them to know that you care,
and that we care.
Show us how to make them feel
that all their work is worthwhile.

WHAT A SILLY SHEEP!

I t wasn't that I meant to cause all that trouble. I just wanted a bit of excitement, that was all. Being a sheep isn't all outings and entertainment, you know – in fact it can be pretty grim. We seem to spend most of our time walking from place to place looking for a bit of decent grass. Now travel's one thing, but what we do is hardly a sight-seeing tour. The only sight we get most of the time is the back view of the sheep in front and, take it from me, there's nothing very exciting about that! Some sheep are even worse off than us, though, they have to put up with some pretty awful shepherds, who don't feed them properly and sometimes even let the wolves get to them. We're lucky there. Our shepherd's good – Joshua's his name. Not all the people like him, but then people are funny that way, aren't they? He's very popular with the sheep. He really cares about us, and a good thing too, or I would have got myself in real trouble by now!

I was always a bit of a rebel – I didn't think God put us on this earth just to follow one another about looking for food – so I was always wandering off looking for excitement. My mother used to get so mad! 'One day,' she used to say to me, 'you'll get into real trouble!' I never believed her. I just longed to be big enough to go off on my own without her stopping me. Then one day I got my chance. We'd stopped for a feed on some juicy grass, and I could see some that was even greener, just up the hill. So off I went and no-one noticed. I was right – it was good stuff. Then I thought, 'If it's like this here, it must be even better further on. So off I trotted and sure enough, there was some lovely grass just the other side of the hill. The trouble was that I soon got lonely. I missed my mum and dad, and all my sisters and my cousins and my aunts in the flock. But when I tried to get back, I couldn't find my way. I was sure I'd gone back over the same hill, but I couldn't have. It was all different. There wasn't much grass and there was no sign of the little stream we'd been drinking at. Well, beautiful green grass is nice enough in its way, but when you've got no-one to share it with, it doesn't seem so much fun. I thought I'd better try in a different direction. But when I got to the next hill, I couldn't see anything I recognised at all.

I was getting really frightened (but don't tell my mum I said that, will you, because she'd only say, 'I told you so!') and I began to think that I'd never get back. All this excitement was getting me down, and walking along looking at the rear view of another sheep seemed like a wonderful idea! As it began to get dark, I thought I'd really had it. On cold nights, we used to huddle together to keep warm and the prospect of being out there on my own, with no-one to snuggle up to, wasn't very nice at all. I thought I'd better try and find a cave to shelter in, just in case it rained. So I tried to turn and look around and had the fright of my life. Somehow, I'd wandered onto the side of a cliff. I was standing on a ledge so narrow there was no way I could turn round. Now I was really scared!

Then, I heard something which really made me prick my ears up. I heard a whistle – oh, not just any old whistle. Joshua had a very special way of whistling to call us back if we were wandering off – and that's what I'd heard. If I hadn't been standing where I was, I'd have jumped for joy, but I decided I'd better not. So I just gave out a little 'baa' and hoped he'd hear me. I heard the whistle again – this time closer than before. So I gave him another 'baa!' and that's how we went on – whistle . . . 'baa' . . . whistle . . . 'baa' until he was at the cliff top just above me. 'You wait there,' he called – as if I'd do anything else – 'and I'll be down to you.' He scrambled down to where I was. 'I don't know how you got here,' he said, 'but I'll get you somewhere safer.' And he picked me up, slung me round his neck and climbed back up. I tell you, I closed my eyes and hung on. That was another thing my parents found embarrassing about me – a sheep that's scared of heights, I ask you!

When we got to the top, I thought Joshua was going to carry me all the way home on his shoulders, like in those lovely pictures you've probably seen, but he put me down. He must have guessed what I was thinking. 'Come on,' he said, 'you walked here, I'm sure you can walk home again. But don't worry, I'll be right with you all the way.' And he was, too – he never left me.

Since that day, I've taken a bit more notice of things – it's not so bad travelling, if you take the trouble to look around. In fact, we get to see some pretty exciting places sometimes. All I have to do is turn my head to the side – can't think why I didn't think of it before!

Based on Luke 15:1-7

Let's Chat

Isn't it good to know that people care for us,
even when we're in trouble and it's our own silly fault!

We're Glad

Thank you, God, for caring for us.
Thank you for telling us that wherever we go,
and whatever we do, you won't forget about us

We're Sad

We know you care about us, Jesus,
and we know we should follow you.
But sometimes, other things seem more exciting,
and we wander off, do our own thing,
then complain when we get into trouble!
Help us to enjoy life, to have fun,
but to stay with you.

Let's Pray for People

People get lost sometimes,
and then others worry about them.
Loving God,
be very close to anxious people,
children who are lost,
parents who are worried about them,
people who have lost their way.
Thank you for people who help:
the police,
the Salvation Army,
and many other organisations.
Help them to go on showing that you care.

WHATEVER YOU'VE DONE, I LOVE YOU

This story is like one that Jesus told, when he wanted to show people what God was like.

Jonathan was a young man who lived with his father, Sam, and his older brother, Enoch. Jonathan and Enoch were very different. Enoch was a serious sort of person, who worked very hard, and Jonathan just wanted to have fun. He often invited his friends home for a party. They used to sing and dance and make lots of noise, and poor Enoch couldn't sleep at all. Sometimes, he would come in and shout at Jonathan, 'Can't you keep the noise down? I've got to be up early in the morning to milk the cows.' But all Jonathan would say was, 'Why bother? You can have a lie in, like I shall – Dad won't mind.' So over the years, Enoch gradually got more and more angry with Jonathan. Sam, their father, would try to get Jonathan to be more grown up, saying things like, 'Some of this will be yours one day, so you really should look after it.'

One day, Jonathan said to Sam, 'You know I don't really want the farm, but I'd quite like my share of your money. Why don't you give it to me now, while I'm young enough to enjoy it?' Sam wasn't sure that would be a good idea, but he thought, 'He's a man now – he's got to make his own life.' So he gave Jonathan a lot of money, and said, 'There, that's your share. Use it well, won't you.' 'Oh I'll use it well!' said Jonathan, his eyes gleaming. And he saddled up a camel and left. Just like that.

Jonathan had heard of a country a long way away where people had lots of fun. There were wild parties every night and everyone loved a man with lots of money. 'Well,' he thought, 'that's me, all right.' So he pointed his camel toward the East, and set off as fast as it would go.

It seemed that everybody had been right. Jonathan had never known parties like it! And he seemed to have lots of friends. Everyone wanted to know this handsome young man with lots of money! Jonathan had a whale of a time! Every night he was at a different party and he spent most of the day sleeping and getting over it. But that didn't matter, because he had so much money he didn't need to work any more. One day, he thought, 'They make beautiful clothes here. I think I'll get myself a few sets.' So he went to the tailor, and set, 'Thirty sets of clothes, please, in the best quality silk.' The tailor was amazed! 'Thirty sets?' he said, 'Are you sure?' 'Yes,' said Jonathan, 'I want a different one for every night of the month.' Then he went to the barber's to get a shave. 'This is good,' he thought, 'I can come here every day – it's better than shaving myself!' So that's what he did. Then he found the games room. They didn't have slot machines in those days – they used people to take your money from you! Jonathan loved playing the games, and he never noticed how much money he was losing. Then one afternoon, he got out of bed thinking, 'I'm going to be late for my shave,' and went to get some money from his bag. What a shock he had – there were only a couple of pounds left! 'I can't get a shave on that,' he thought, 'more to the point, I can't even get much food for it.'

Jonathan thought long and hard about what to do. 'I've got lots of friends,' he thought, 'they will help me.' That was his second shock. They all said things like, 'Sorry, Jonathan, but I've just paid the baker and I haven't any money in the house,' or, 'Well, I'd like to help you, but my wife wouldn't like it.' Then the word got around that Jonathan had run out of money and his friends seemed to disappear. They were never at home when he called and they never came to see him. He sold his lovely clothes back to the tailor, but for a tenth of what he'd paid for them. Before long, he was looking scruffy and dirty, and no-one wanted to know him. 'I'd better get a job,' he thought, 'before I starve to death.' The only job he could get was for a farmer who wanted a pig-man. The wages were so bad that he still couldn't afford food. 'I'll end up eating the pigswill at this rate,' he thought. Then he had an idea. 'My father pays his workers well,' he thought, 'I wonder if he'd take me back as a worker?' So, without waiting another moment, he got up and started the long journey home. On the way, he planned out what he was going to say when he arrived. 'I'm sorry Dad,' he would say, 'I don't deserve to be your son any more, because I've been very silly.

Can you give me a job – I'll work really hard this time, I promise.'

As Jonathan got to the edge of his father's farm, he saw Sam on the roof-top, looking towards him. Sam had been there every day, hoping to see Jonathan coming back. When he saw his son, he was overjoyed. He went running to meet him and gave him a big hug. Jonathan never got the chance to say what he'd planned. His father called a servant. 'Look who's here,' he said, 'don't just stand there, go and get him some decent clothes – and organise a party. My son's come home!' Jonathan's brother Enoch heard the noise and came to see what was happening.' What's going on?' he asked. 'We're having a party,' said a servant, 'Jonathan's back.' Enoch was hopping mad! 'What are you doing,' he shouted at Sam. 'I've worked for you all these years and got no credit for it, and now this lousy son of yours comes home and you throw a party – after all he's done!' Sam said, 'He's your brother, you know, as well as my son. You know you can have anything you want from me. But right now we're celebrating because Jonathan seemed to be gone for good, and now he's back. Won't you come in and be happy with us?' 'Not on your life!' said Enoch, and stormed off.

There was a wonderful party that night, Everyone enjoyed it – except Enoch. He just stood outside, listening to the sounds. Deep down, he wanted to go in, but he was so jealous that he stayed outside and sulked, and made himself even more unhappy. His father couldn't persuade him to go in.

Wasn't that a shame?

Based on Luke 15:11-32

Let's Chat

Whatever we've done, God loves us!

We're Glad

Heavenly Father,
thank you for loving us.
Thank you for the people
who love us, (especially . . .)
We try to do the things
that will please you,
because we love you.
But even when we get things wrong,
you still love us. Thank you

We're Sad

We get angry with people, sometimes.
Sometimes, we're so angry
that when they say, 'sorry', we ignore them.
Then we make ourselves unhappy,
as well as them.
We're sorry that we can't love people
as much as you do.
Help us to be like Jonathan's father,
and not like his older brother.

Let's Pray for People

Let's pray for people who are angry,
so angry that it hurts.
Loving Father,
help people who are angry.
Perhaps they have a good reason.
Perhaps they've been badly hurt.
But help them to forgive,
the way you do,
so that they can be happy themselves.

DON'T JUST SIT THERE

*H*ave your legs ever felt like jelly – perhaps because you were frightened or had a shock? Well, that's how it was for Jamie – except that his legs were always like that. He couldn't stand on them at all. Of course, there were many things he could do – the rest of his body was fine, and his brain was first rate – but it was just his legs. They wouldn't seem to work at all! He'd been to lots of different doctors and no-one could help. The real problem was that in those days, you needed legs even more than you do now. There were no wheelchairs, and no-one considered disabled people at all, when they were building houses, or offices – or even the temple. They just went on as though everyone could walk and climb steps, and they ignored people like Jamie. So it was very difficult for anyone who was disabled.

Jamie had an ambition. 'I could be an accountant,' he used to say, 'and help everybody else look after their money. I don't need my legs to do sums!' That was true, of course, but before he could do that, Jamie needed money himself, and it was difficult for him to earn any. So, every day, some friends of his would carry him to the temple in Jerusalem. They would sit him down by one of the gates, which everyone called 'the Beautiful Gate' (can you guess why?), and Jamie would sit there, hoping people would give him some money. He hated it! It was so embarrassing! 'Why should I have to do this?' he used to think, 'I've got a first class brain, and I can use my hands, but you'd think I was completely useless, just because my legs won't work!'

One day, at about three in the afternoon, Peter and John were on their way to the temple, to worship God. Jesus had gone back to heaven, but he'd told them that he'd always be with them, although they couldn't see him. He'd also given them work to do, before he left. So Peter and John were talking about what they should do.

'We've got to tell everybody about Jesus,' John was saying, 'tell them all the things he did and said.' 'Yes,' said Peter, 'and we've got to tell them who he was.' 'The point is,'

John went on, 'that Jesus has shown us what God is like. If people knew that God was like Jesus, they'd love him more and be a lot less frightened of him.' Peter agreed. John went on, 'The question is, how do we actually show them that?' Peter replied, 'We've got to let Jesus use our hands to help people, and use our mouths to speak to them.' 'Good idea,' said John, 'and before we do that, we've got to let him use our ears to listen to them. That man over there, for example – what's he saying?' John had noticed Jamie, sitting at the Beautiful Gate, and calling out, 'Spare me some money, please,' to the people who went in.

Peter and John went over to Jamie. 'Hello,' said John, 'what do you want?' Jamie thought, 'They must be deaf, I've been calling out loudly enough.' Out loud, he said, 'I need money – just enough for some food.' 'I know you need money,' said Peter, 'but what do you *really* want?' 'Oh, that's a very different matter!' said Jamie, 'I want to be able to stand up on these silly legs of mine. I want to be able to talk to people without craning my neck, and without them bending down to me as if I were a baby in a pram! I want to be able to walk into that temple on my own two legs and worship God, I want to be able to run, and jump, and kick a ball like anyone else. I want . . .' 'Yes, I get the picture!' laughed John. 'You want a good pair of legs.' 'Fat chance of that, though,' said Jamie, 'so I suppose money will have to do.' 'Well, we haven't got any money,' said Peter. Jamie was really disappointed – after all that, these two fellows were just going to go into the temple without giving him anything at all! But before he could speak, Peter went on, 'but I can give you something else: in the name of Jesus, get up and walk.' Before Jamie could ask what was going on, he felt a tingling in his toes. He couldn't understand it – he'd never felt anything in his toes before! Then the tingling spread – up to his ankles, then to his knees, and then it felt as though the whole of each leg was burning. And what do you do if you burn your foot? You jump around a bit! So that's what Jamie did! Then he realised. 'Wow!' he said, 'I'm standing up! What happened.' 'God made your legs better – that's what happened,' said John. 'Well, we'd better go and say thank you, properly!'

shouted Jamie, and grabbed hold of Peter and John and dragged them into the temple. People were amazed. 'That's the man who used to be at the Beautiful gate!' someone said. 'Yes,' said someone else, 'he's obviously been cured!' Everyone was amazed.

Peter and John were very pleased as well. 'That's because we did what Jesus would have done,' said John. 'You mean, when we healed his legs?' asked Peter. 'No,' said John, 'when we listened to what he really wanted.' 'That's right,' said Peter, 'just think, if we'd had any money to give him, he might still be sitting there!'

Based on Acts 3:1-10

Let's Chat

Isn't it nice when people really listen to us?
Perhaps we ought to try really listening to them!

We're Glad

Thank you, loving God,
for teaching people to listen.
Thank you for caring
about our real needs.
Thank you for helping us
to care for others
in the same way.

We're Sad

There are times when we don't listen.
Sometimes, we think we know best
what someone else needs.
Sometimes, we treat disabled people
as though they were invalids.
And they're not!
We're sorry if we hurt people,
please help us to listen
the way you do.

Let's Pray for People

Some people just don't get listened to.
They may be given things,
they may even be cared for,
but they don't get listened to.
Please God, help people to listen.
And when we've listened,
show us how we can help.

Index of Bible References

OLD TESTAMENT

NEW TESTAMENT